IV-F

*A Guide to
Medical,
Psychiatric,
and
Moral Unfitness Standards
for Military Induction*

by David Suttler

GROVE PRESS, INC.   NEW YORK

They wrote in the old days
that it is sweet and fitting
to die for one's country.
But in modern war
there is nothing sweet
nor fitting in your dying.
You will die like a dog
for no good reason.

ERNEST HEMINGWAY
"Notes on the Next War"

Contents

Introduction

"LOTTERY! THE STAR-SPANGLED GAME OF THRILLS and spills that has every young man in America figuring the odds. What are your chances of being wiped out in Gookland? Can you make it around the Year Board without drawing the Greetings Card? Or landing on Jail Square? Play this exciting new game by the Selective Service Bros. Certain to please those aged 19 to 26."

What the Selective Service Bros. fail to make clear is that *you* are still the pawn. They still claim the right to make you fight a war you loathe, and to put you in jail if you say no. You *can* decline to play. But few have the courage or commitment to refuse induction.

There is another alternative—have the military

refuse you. The Army's own fitness standards make every potential draftee a potential draft reject.

It is quite possible that you have a medical defect or psychiatric condition which would disqualify you from military service and you don't even know about it. The Army is not likely to find it for you at the preinduction physical—a haphazard mass inspection apparently designed to uncover only the most glaring faults. But a knowledge of the unfitness criteria and a visit to a private physician could keep you out of uniform. It could also save the government the expense of inducting and training someone who is not qualified.

Unfortunately, the average draft registrant, lacking a seriously debilitating affliction, is likely to assume he meets the Army's standards. In reality, one need not be a candidate for the insane asylum or confined to a wheel chair to obtain a medical exemption. There is no reason why anyone should report for his physical without a disability claim.

Nor is it absolutely necessary to have a physical or psychiatric problem to be rejected. Registrants with a criminal or subversive background can escape the draft as "moral rejects." There is also a mental test for induction. The Army's intelligence standards, however, are so low it is doubtful that anyone able to read this book could manage to flunk it.

The new lottery law does not alter the fitness standards. Neither will it increase or decrease the number of young men drafted. It changes only the process by which they are selected.

All who reached their 19th birthday but not their 26th by 1 January 1970 were assigned a number in the first drawing (see Random Selection Sequence table in Appendix). The number they received will always be theirs, no matter what year they enter the draft pool. In future lotteries, only 19-year-olds will be affected.

Youths will be drafted in the order their birthdays were picked. Those born on the same day of the year will be called in the order the initials of their last names were selected in another drawing.

Deferments remain in effect, and no one will be inducted as long as he has one. His lottery number will decide his chances of being drafted in the year his deferment ends.

The lottery is a major reform. It brings to an end the cruel system that left all youths to wonder for seven years whether the draft would strike. Instead, everyone will now be vulnerable for one year only, and if not called up in that year, safe from the draft forever (unless there is a "national emergency").

But the prime inequity of the draft continues: involuntary military servitude. And despite the lottery, the system is still unfair. Deferments remain available to a privileged few. Unrepresentative local boards retain most of their arbitrary powers, ungoverned by uniform national guidelines. Registrants are denied elementary due process: the right to counsel in appearances before their boards and, in most cases, to court review of their draft classifications.

As in the past, the Selective Service System's most potent weapon is confusion. You are invited to contact your local board for "information and advice," but it is unlikely you will be able to obtain either. Therefore, explanations of some of the complexities of the lottery system are offered in the following series of questions and answers.

Q. Which lottery will decide my number and when will I be subject to induction?

A. If you were born between 1 January 1944 and 31 December 1950 your number was assigned in the 1969 drawing. If you have no deferment, you will be vulnerable to the draft during 1970 only. Those not in the 1969 drawing will receive their numbers in the lottery which takes place during the year of their 19th birthday and will be subject to induction the following year—the one in which their 20th birthday falls.

Q. What happens if I turn 26 in the year I become vulnerable to the draft?

A. If your number is reached before your birthday, you will be inducted if found fit. Once you pass 26, you are draft free, even if your number comes up later in the year. If you have ever been deferred, you are technically liable to induction until age 35, but all registrants under 26 must be called by your local board before you can be called.

Q. Which numbers will be called?

A. In any year it will depend on the size of the draft calls. For 1970, everyone has a different answer. The Pentagon says those assigned numbers below 122 are doomed, numbers above 245 safe, and those in between a toss-up. But many state draft directors warn not even the highest numbers are out of danger, and several local boards insist they'll have to go right up to 366 to meet their quotas. So much for Nixon's claim that the lottery would eliminate uncertainty. However, even if your number is 1, you can't be taken unless found fit.

Q. I have a deferment which ends in November. Am I only vulnerable to the draft for two months?

A. You cannot be inducted until your deferment ends, but if your number was called earlier in the year, you will be drafted almost immediately. The only difference between your position and that of anyone else with your number is that those who had no deferment would have been summoned at the time the number came up.

Q. Is there a loophole?

A. Not really. If you have a deferment, you can wait until late in a year, see if your number is likely to be called, and drop your deferment if things look good. If not taken that year, your worries are over. However, it may take your local board several months to reclassify you. Thus, if you wait late enough to be sure your number is safe, your deferment might end not in the remaining months of the year you asked it to be withdrawn, but in the beginning of the next year—leaving 11 or 12 months of uncertainty.[1]

An unpopular war, like the struggle in Vietnam, cannot be waged without military conscription. If our policy-makers had to depend on volunteers, no war could be launched unless young men were willing to fight it. But the draft allows strategists to draw battle plans in the confidence that a ready—if not willing—source of manpower is always at hand.

Even in time of peace, perhaps especially then, the draft is unacceptable in a democratic society. Through the threat of induction and the seduction of deferments, the Selective Service manages to regiment even those it fails to enslave.

There are those who argue that effective resistance depends on filling the jails with young men who refuse induction. But not all men are martyrs. The draft is vulnerable at many points—none should be neglected.

If you have an out, are you morally justified in taking it? For the youth who opposes a system that makes him a soldier against his will, orders him to kill on command, forces him to fight a war his conscience cannot abide, the answer should be obvious.

This book cannot stop the war. Its only aim is to help those who dissent. Designed as a practical guide for those who do not feel they should have to wear either military khaki or prison stripes, it provides:

* a comprehensive list of medical unfitness standards, taken from the Army's official regulations
* a description of some disqualifying defects even your own doctor may not discover unless they are called to his attention
* a discussion of psychiatric problems most commonly accepted as grounds for rejection
* a guide to medical groups whose members have taken a sympathetic approach to the problems of draft registrants
* an analysis of the moral standards used to determine fitness for induction
* step-by-step directions for pressing your disability claim
* a description of the official rules for, and the reality of, the preinduction physical examination
* a detailed guide to your rights in appealing a medical classification and claiming a medical discharge and pension if inducted

The handbook is based on Selective Service and military regulations, legal and medical research, and numerous interviews with government officials, attorneys, physicians, and psychiatrists experienced in the field. It is intended for the draft registrant and the doctor, both of whom in most cases lack the necessary information to deal effectively with the exemption problem. It is written in the hope that no potential IV-F dies fighting a war to which he is opposed.

1

Rx for Resisters

YOU CANNOT BE DRAFTED UNTIL YOU HAVE PASSED your preinduction physical. The odds are four to one you won't fail that examination on medical grounds. The youth who wanders through his physical ignorant of the standards by which he will be judged is thus likely to find himself in uniform a few months later.

But the odds against obtaining a medical or psychiatric exemption can be improved dramatically.

The first thing to understand is that you don't have to be unhealthy to be unfit. Professional athletes are often draft rejects. You can turn cartwheels all the way to the examining station and do twenty push-ups while the doctor is checking for hemorrhoids, and never receive an induction notice if you:

* have hemorrhoids, flat feet, or a severe ingrown toenail
* stutter, stammer, or have "an impaired characterological capacity to adapt to military service"
* wear extensive or obscene tattoos

While the authorities provide no criteria for determining whether tattoos have crossed the line from acceptable social commentary to obscenity, the Army, by law, is required to make public its official list of medical fitness standards.[1]

A careful reading of that list (reprinted in Chapter Two) is your first step toward exemption. As the sampling above indicates, the list contains many surprising causes for rejection. There are medical and psychiatric problems which, while only annoying in civilian life, could seriously limit an individual's ability to adapt to Army life.

If you have a listed defect or condition you cannot be drafted.[2] It is the Army and not the Selective Service which determines acceptability. And the Army is reluctant to induct someone who claims a medical problem which might make him ineligible for military service after a few days of basic training, but eligible for a disability pension for life. When the ailment is of a doubtful nature, this factor works in the registrant's favor.

Although this nation is at war in Vietnam, it is the peacetime fitness standards which apply. Under these standards, all those with defects which would preclude training, might be aggravated by military duty, or whose treatment would interfere with Army routine are unacceptable.[3]

If you believe that you may have one of the listed

defects (and there are more than four hundred to choose from), your next step should take you to a private physician or psychiatrist. Because a medical history of your ailment could be crucial, don't wait until you are called for a physical to visit a doctor.

If your family physician is cooperative, he might be the best man to see. He may have treated you in the past for the condition you wish to document, or for problems which can be related to it. However, the political leanings of the doctor could be as significant as the nature of your disability, and too much familiarity with your medical background may not prove beneficial. Be alert to the possibility of an unfavorable bias. While one physician might find ample reason to consider your condition a disqualification for military service, another might see the same condition as a minor problem which should not be allowed to interfere with your induction.

Because doctors are a basically conservative group, finding a sympathetic physician could pose a problem. Since psychiatric judgments are more subjective, the psychiatrist's bias is especially important. Fortunately, an understanding psychiatrist will usually be somewhat easier to locate. Of course, if your defect is obvious and specifically listed as disqualifying, the physician could belong to the American Legion.

In most urban areas there are medical groups whose members have taken a sympathetic position in dealing with the problems of draft-age youths. These include:

* Medical Committee for Human Rights—the most active in this field, with chapters in cities throughout the country (See Appendix 11)
* Physicians for Social Responsibility

* Student Health Organization
* Medical Resistance Union—organized to aid doctors seeking alternatives to military service

These groups are often loosely organized and in many cases will not even have an office or a telephone number. But member doctors and other physicians with similar leanings can usually be located through local draft resistance unions. If there is a free (hippie) clinic in your area, it too is likely to be of some assistance.

A model project to aid draft registrants with potentially disqualifying medical problems has been established in Boston through the cooperation of the city's Draft Resistance Group and the Medical Committee for Human Rights. Youths are screened by the DRG and referred to the appropriate physician or psychiatrist.

"I just follow the Army's own standards," commented a physician connected with the Boston project. "I'm sure the Army appreciates my help in screening out unsuitable prospects." A New York doctor, whose efforts have won more than fifty exemptions, put it this way: "The traditional doctor-patient relationship is one of preserving life. I save lives by keeping people out of the Army."

It is unlikely, however, that the doctor you see will feel quite this way, and your attitude in dealing with him should not appear to be, "I'm here for my IV-F."

On the other hand, you will need a letter. Documentation of your unfitness is essential—perhaps more important than the defect itself. You are more likely to win an exemption with a doctor's letter describing a disqualifying defect that does not exist, than with the condition and no report. Army regulations clearly state that "in no case will a registrant be found disqualified for induction solely on his unsupported claim of a disqualifying defect."

Obtaining a letter from your doctor should present no great problem. Simply tell him that you have received an order to report for your physical and it says to bring a physician's certification of any condition which may disqualify you from military service. He's more likely to be cooperative if your health rather than the draft seems your primary concern. (There is, of course, no reason to hide your draft anxieties from a psychiatrist, who will no doubt be interested in all your hangups.)

The wording of the letter can be decisive. It should follow that of the official standards as closely as possible. While no physician will appreciate your making a diagnosis for him, it could be helpful if you are prepared to answer any questions he might have concerning the Army's standards and the kinds of activity required by military duty which your condition would make it difficult for you to perform.

In no case should your letter be sent anywhere before you have a chance to see it. One psychiatrist whose clients include many draft age youths noted that he has seen letters written by colleagues which say, in effect, "Here is John Smith for induction." Seeking the opinion of a second doctor would seem advisable in these circumstances. (If a draft registrant has retained an attorney to assist him in his efforts to remain a civilian, the lawyer should discuss his case with the physician, just as he would in handling a personal injury claim.)

Many exemptions have been won with notes

scrawled on a prescription pad, but most letters
should include:

* * a description of the disqualifying condition and
  recommended treatment
* * a full statement of past history
* * if possible, the doctor's professional judgment
  that the disability would impair military performance and/or be aggravated by such duty
* * the physician's professional qualifications, especially if he has served in the Armed Forces or
  Public Health Service

If the patient has had any problems in civilian life
—his activity restricted, his employment or school-
work adversely affected—these should be mentioned.
If a youth with a back condition has had trouble
lifting heavy objects, a description of this is the best
way to indicate his inability to complete basic training. The incapacitating nature of migraine headaches
might be illustrated by the patient's forced absences
from classes. Failure to hold down a job for an extended time could be used as evidence of instability
in a psychiatrist's report. If continued medical attention is called for, this should be stated.

As already indicated, the letter need not be lengthy
—three or four paragraphs could be sufficient—and
medical records (laboratory and X-ray findings),
while helpful if available, are rarely, if ever, required. The note should, however, be dated not
more than a month prior to the time it is presented.
(If your unfitness is debatable, it helps to have your
claim supported by a second physician. A college
student might, for example, obtain one letter from
a doctor at school and another from one in his
hometown.)

With the defect, doctor, and documentation in hand, you are ready to claim your exemption. To do so, you can either wait to be called for your preinduction physical or request your draft board to arrange a medical interview.

If your defect is well established and meets the official unfitness criteria, the medical interview route is best. Your disability claim will receive greater attention and you will get your exemption earlier.

If, on the other hand, yours is a borderline case, a thorough examination of your disqualifying condition might not prove beneficial; wait for your physical where an overburdened examiner will be more inclined simply to accept the findings of your private physician.

In either case, your fitness will be judged by the Army's standards. But at a preinduction physical the Army will also decide whether you are disqualified; a medical interview will result in your local board making that determination.[4] And every board must fill its quota with qualified registrants.

There is another factor to consider. By demanding a medical interview you are putting your draft board on notice: I want out! Your appearance at a preinduction physical is, on the other hand, required, and the notice to report clearly instructs you to bring evidence of medical problems.

Under Selective Service regulations your right to a medical interview is plain (unless you have a deferment):

> Whenever a registrant who is in Class I-A [available], Class I-A-O [noncombatant only], or Class I-O [conscientious objector] claims that he has one or more of the disqualifying medical conditions or

physical defects which appear in [the Army's official list], the local board shall order him to present himself for interview with the medical advisor to the local board at the time and place specified by the local board . . .[5]

In practice, however, many draft boards fail to grant medical interviews and simply order those who request one to an early physical. If your medical interview request is ignored or denied, you may seek the aid of the Selective Service Director in your state. It probably will not help.

To arrange a medical interview, send a registered letter to your local board similar to the following: "In accordance with Section 1628.2(b) of the Selective Service Regulations, I wish to appear for a medical interview because I have [name of defect], a disqualifying condition under section ———— of AR 40-501."

You must enclose the letter from your doctor, but be sure to photocopy it first. And, as in all other correspondence with your board, include your Selective Service number.

Once granted, the medical interview is no longer voluntary. Unless you are too ill, you must appear when and where told. (If you live far from your local board, the examination can be transferred to a board in your area.)[6]

A civilian physician (medical adviser) selected by the draft board will examine you only to determine if the claimed defect exists. Normally, he will not be a specialist and is barred by regulations from performing any laboratory or X-ray work.[7] But you can strengthen your case by submitting your own doctor's records. In any event, bring a copy of your doctor's letter; the one you mailed may not have reached the physician who examines you.

The medical adviser's opinion of your fitness is not binding on the local board, which, if no doctor is available, will itself handle the medical interview.

There are three possible verdicts the board can render: unacceptable for military service, acceptable, or status undetermined. The decision is final only if you are found unacceptable. If the board rejects your unfitness claim or "has any doubt concerning the existence of any such condition," it must order you to report for a regular preinduction physical.[8]

Because a medical interview cannot result in acceptance yet can win an exemption, it might be assumed that all should have one. But there is a catch—an adverse ruling by your board will appear in your records at your physical and could have a bad influence on the Army medical examiner.

You cannot be inducted or ordered to perform alternative service as a conscientious objector until you have had your physical examination.[9] (In the past, registrants declared delinquent could be drafted without a physical, but a recent Supreme Court ruling forbids such action.)

Any draft registrant can be called for a physical at any time; all should consider their exemption possibilities early. Some boards routinely have college students examined, not to strip them of their deferments but simply to determine their future eligibility. Ordinarily, however, only those classified I-A (or as conscientious objectors) are called.

If an order to report finds you unprepared for your physical, try to have it delayed. This can be done in two ways: by seeking a formal postponement through your local board or by having the examination transferred. The transfer method is best because it is practically automatic for registrants absent from their local board areas with "good reason."

For a formal postponement, file a written request with your board. It must be based on illness (note from doctor required), a death in the immediate family, or "an extreme emergency" beyond your control involving yourself or your immediate family. If the request is denied, appeal immediately to your State Director. The postponement can be for a maximum of sixty days, will usually be shorter, and may be revoked at any time your board decides your induction is imminent.[10]

If you are living, working, or going to school in one city and your local board is in another, you can transfer your physical simply by dropping in at the nearest board. Tell them your problem, fill out the form, and wait for your new orders to come. This action will usually put off the examination for at least a month, although the board with which you file your request can deny the transfer.[11]

If you are ordered to a physical while abroad, you can be examined at the nearest Army base rather than return to the states. But don't float in with a letter from your doctor in Katmandu, because only notes from American physicians "need be considered."

The preinduction physical is a haphazard and confusing affair. Scared youths, up before dawn and stripped to their underwear, are ordered about by men in uniform. An unwary registrant can easily find the examination completed before he has claimed his disability.

Bring your doctor's letter to the physical, even if a copy has already been sent to your draft board, and hold on to it as though your life depended on it. It might. When told to undress, you will be given a cloth bag for your valuables to carry throughout the examination; put the letter in the bag (a better place than in the waistband of your shorts). At each step ask to whom it should be presented. Do not give the note to anyone until you are sure you have reached the right doctor.

He will probably ask you to describe your current health. Tell him it is poor, noting the nature of your unfitness, and show him the letter, even if he does not ask to see it. Characteristically, he will not make an extensive effort to determine if the claimed condition exists; his examination is likely to consist of a brief interview rather than clinical or laboratory tests. If your problem is psychiatric, the Army doctor (who often will not be a psychiatrist) will probably ask just a few perfunctory questions.

At this point, whatever the claimed condition, the physician will usually tell you if you have been found unfit. If he does not, ask him. Medical examiners are specifically prohibited by Army regulations from waiving the official standards unless you request it, and you must be disqualified if you have a listed defect.[12] (If found acceptable, appeal immediately; the procedure is set out in Chapter Seven.)

Once disqualified, your worries are over. Your draft board cannot overrule the Army examiner, and neither the Army nor the Selective Service attempts detective-type investigations of medical rejects (there are very rare exceptions). Explained a spokesman for Selective Service headquarters, "As long as there are plenty of men available, no one's going to spend any time investigating hippies."

It is highly unlikely that officials will even bother to check back with the doctor who wrote the letter. Among the physicians interviewed for this book— some of whom have written almost as many draft-exemption letters as prescriptions—none had ever been asked if they actually wrote the notes; a few had been requested to forward relevant records, but when they replied that the patient's permission would be required, the matter was never pursued.

Formal notification of your hard-earned exemption will arrive by mail via your local board, whose only responsibilities are to record the results of the physical and seal the envelopes.

There are two types of classifications given to the unfit:

* Class I-Y—draft exempt except in time of *declared* war or national emergency:

   In Class I-Y shall be placed any registrant who . . . would be classified I-A, Class I-A-O, or Class I-O but for the fact that he is found under applicable physical, mental, and moral standards to be not currently qualified for service in the Armed Forces and who would be qualified for such service in time of war or national emergency declared by the Congress.[13]

* Class IV-F—total immunity from military service:

   In Class IV-F shall be placed any registrant who is found under applicable physical, mental, and moral standards to be not qualified for any service in the Armed Forces either currently or in time of war or national emergency declared by the Congress.[14]

IV-F is obviously the more desirable of the two classifications. It is a permanent, irrevocable, and unconditional release from the draft. To be designated IV-F a registrant must have a physical or psychiatric problem so disabling as to be unacceptable cannon fodder even in time of full mobilization.

A I-Y, however, will serve quite well in times of peace or undeclared war. No induction notice will arrive unless Congress formally declares war. The Vietnam struggle is undeclared; I-Y's cannot be called to fight it.

There are, in effect, two types of I-Y's: permanent —for those with conditions considered chronic, but not serious enough to bar induction in time of full mobilization; temporary—for registrants with physical or psychiatric problems from which they are likely to recover. It is advisable, therefore, for I-Y's to continue visiting their private physicians. An uninterrupted medical history could be valuable if called for a second physical. While Army medical examiners indicate that periodic rechecking is justified only for those in the temporary group, it is the local board's prerogative to decide who gets a second call.[15] When manpower needs increase, all I-Y's are subject to re-examination and risk losing their exemptions unless the disqualifying defect persists.

"The condition upon which God hath given liberty to man," as John Philpot Curran observed, "is eternal vigilance; which condition if he break, servitude is at once the consequence . . ."

2

Medical Unfitness

"The Surgeon General of the Department of the Army," Selective Service regulations declare, "shall, from time to time, prescribe or approve a list enumerating various medical conditions or physical defects that disqualify registrants for service in the Armed Forces."

That list is published by the Army as AR 40-501, Standards of Medical Fitness. The current criteria for induction are set forth in Chapter Two of the official publication and are reprinted below.* (The

* Wherever possible technical medical terms have been explained in simple language. The original wording of the official publication has been retained and the explanatory material placed in brackets (e.g., *Cholecystectomy* [gall bladder removal]). Psychiatric unfitness standards are reprinted in

section numbers used in AR 40-501 have been retained in this book and should be noted in all correspondence with the Army and Selective Service.)

The listed disabilities are the "causes for rejection
for military service in peacetime." By peacetime, the
Army means both actual tranquillity and undeclared
war, such as the Vietnam conflict. Were Congress
to declare war, a set of mobilization fitness standards
permitting fewer exemptions would apply.

Even if you do not have a specifically listed defect,
you may be unfit. The officially stated objective for
Chapter Two of AR 40-501 is to ensure that draftees
will be:

1. free of contagious or infectious diseases which
would be likely to endanger the health of other personnel

2. free of medical conditions or physical defects
which would require excessive time lost from duty
by reason of necessary treatment or hospitalization
or most probably result in separation from the service by reason of medical unfitness

3. medically capable of satisfactorily completing
required training

4. medically adaptable to the military environment
without the necessity of geographical area limitations

5. medically capable of performing duties without
aggravation of existing physical defects or medical
conditions[1]

Chapter Four of this book. Omitted from the list in this
chapter are those items that refer to the enlistment and
appointment of women.

MEDICAL FITNESS STANDARDS FOR APPOINTMENT, ENLISTMENT, AND INDUCTION

SECTION II. ABDOMEN AND GASTROINTESTINAL SYSTEM

2-3. Abdominal Organs and Gastrointestinal System   The causes for rejection for appointment, enlistment, and induction are:

a. Cholecystectomy [gall bladder removal], sequelae of [complications of], such as postoperative stricture [narrowing] of the common bile duct, reforming of stones in hepatic or common bile ducts, or incisional hernia, or postcholecystectomy syndrome when symptoms are so severe as to interfere with normal performance of duty.

b. Cholecystitis [gall bladder infection and inflammation], acute or chronic, with or without cholelithiasis [gallstones], if diagnosis is confirmed by usual laboratory procedures or authentic medical records.

c. Cirrhosis, regardless of the absence of manifestations such as jaundice, ascites [abdominal fluid] or known esophageal varices [enlarged veins in esophagus], abnormal liver function tests with or without history of chronic alcoholism.

d. Fistula in ano [slit in anus].

e. Gastritis [inflammation of walls of stomach], chronic hypertrophic, severe.

f. Hemorrhoids.

   (1) External hemorrhoids producing marked symptoms [bleeding, pain, protrusion].

(2) Internal hemorrhoids, if large or accompanied with hemorrhage or protruding intermittently or constantly.

g. Hepatitis within the preceding six months, or persistence of symptoms after a reasonable period of time with objective evidence of impairment of liver function.

h. Hernia [rupture].

(1) Hernia other than small asymptomatic umbilical or hiatal [protrusion of stomach through a gap in diaphragm].

(2) History of operation for hernia within the preceding sixty days.

i. Intestinal obstruction or authenticated history of more than one episode, if either occurred during the preceding five years, or if resulting condition remains which produces significant symptoms or requires treatment.

j. Megacolon [enlarged colon] of more than minimal degree, *diverticulitis* [inflammation of pouches found along large intestine], *regional enteritis* [inflammation of small intestine], and *ulcerative colitis* [inflammation of large intestine]. *Irritable colon* [intermittent spasm of large intestine resulting in cramps and frequent bowel movements] of more than moderate degree.

k. Pancreas, acute or chronic disease of, if proven by laboratory tests, or authenticated medical records.

l. Rectum, stricture [narrowing] or prolapse [protrusion] of.

m. Resection, gastric or of bowel [surgical removal of all or part of stomach or intestine]; *or gastroenterostomy* [one type of operation performed for ulcers]; however minimal intestinal re-section in infancy or childhood (*for example*: for intussusception [turning back of the intestine into itself] or pyloric stenosis [narrowing of part of stomach leading to bowel]) is acceptable if the individual has been asymptomatic since the resection and if surgical consultation (to include upper and lower gastrointestinal series) gives complete clearance.

n. Scars.

(1) Scars, abdominal, regardless of cause, which show hernial bulging or which interfere with movements.

(2) Scar pain associated with disturbances of function of abdominal wall or contained viscera [organs in the abdomen].

o. Sinuses [chronic perforation] of abdominal wall.

p. Splenectomy [removal of spleen], except when accomplished for the following:

(1) Trauma.

(2) Causes unrelated to diseases of the spleen.

(3) Hereditary spherocytosis [blood dis-order].

(4) Disease involving the spleen when fol-lowed by correction of a condition for a period of at least two years.

q. Tumors. See paragraphs 2-40 and 2-41.

r. Ulcer.

(1) Ulcer of the stomach or duodenum, if diagnosis is confirmed by X-ray examination, or authenticated history thereof.

(2) Authentic history of surgical opera-tion(s) for gastric or duodenal ulcer.

s. Other congenital or acquired abnormalities and defects which preclude satisfactory performance of military duty or which require frequent and prolonged treatment.

SECTION III. BLOOD AND BLOOD-FORMING TISSUE DISEASES

2-4. Blood and Blood-Forming Tissue Diseases The causes for rejection for appointment, enlistment, and induction are:

a. Anemia [low red cell count in blood].

(1) Blood loss anemia—until both condition and basic cause are corrected.

(2) Deficiency anemia [caused by lack of specific substance required to make red blood cells], not controlled by medication.

(3) Abnormal destruction of RBC's [red blood cells]: hemolytic anemia.

(4) Faulty RBC construction: hereditary hemolytic anemia, thalassemia and sickle-cell anemia.

(5) Myelophthisic anemia [destruction of bone marrow]: Myelomatosis, leukemia, Hodgkin's disease.

(6) Primary refractory anemia: Aplastic anemia, DiGuglielmo's syndrome.

b. Hemorrhagic states [bleeding states].

(1) Due to changes in coagulation [clotting] system (hemophilia, etc.).

(2) Due to platelet [blood particle involved in clotting] deficiency.

(3) Due to vascular instability [blood vessel abnormality].

c. Leukopenia [white cell deficiency], chronic or recurrent, associated with increased susceptibility to infection.

d. Myeloproliferative [abnormal bone marrow] *disease (other than leukemia).*

(1) Myelofibrosis [scarring of bone marrow].

(2) Megakaryocytic myelosis [blood disorder].

(3) Polycythemia vera [too many red blood cells].

e. Splenomegaly [enlarged spleen] until the cause is remedied.

f. Thromboembolic disease [clots in blood vessels] except for acute, nonrecurrent conditions.

SECTION IV. DENTAL

2-5. Dental The causes for rejection for appointment, enlistment, and induction are:

a. Diseases of the jaws or associated tissues which are not easily remediable and which will incapacitate the individual or prevent the satisfactory performance of military duty.

b. Malocclusion [malalignment of jaws], severe, which interferes with the mastication [chewing] of a normal diet.

c. Oral tissues, extensive loss of, in an amount that would prevent replacement of missing teeth with a satisfactory prosthetic appliance [false teeth].

d. Orthodontic appliances. [The criteria are listed separately in paragraph 7-12 of the government regulations but are printed here for your convenience.]

Individuals with orthodontic appliances attached

are administratively unacceptable for [enlistment or induction] as long as active treatment is required.

Individuals with retainer orthodontic appliances who are not required to undergo active treatment are administratively acceptable for appointment, enlistment, or induction.

e. Relationship between the mandible [lower jaw] and maxilla [upper jaw] of such a nature as to preclude future satisfactory prosthodontic replacement.

Section V. Ears and Hearing

2-6. Ears   The causes for rejection for appointment, enlistment, and induction are:

a. Auditory canal.

(1) Atresia [absence or closure] or severe stenosis [narrowing] of the external auditory canal.

(2) Tumors of the external auditory canal except mild exostoses [bone protrusion].

(3) Severe external otitis [ear infection], acute or chronic.

b. Auricle [outer ear]: Agenesis [absence or underdevelopment], severe; or severe traumatic [due to injury] deformity, unilateral or bilateral [one or both ears].

c. Mastoids.

(1) Mastoiditis [infection of sinuses in bone behind ear], acute or chronic.

(2) Residual of mastoid operation with marked external deformity which precludes or interferes with the wearing of a gas mask or helmet.

(3) Mastoid fistula [perforation of mastoid].

d. Ménière's syndrome [see Chapter Three].

e. Middle ear.

(1) Acute or chronic suppurative otitis media [pus-producing middle-ear infection]. Individuals with a recent history of acute suppurative otitis media will not be accepted unless the condition is healed and a sufficient interval of time subsequent to treatment has elapsed to insure that the disease is in fact not chronic.

(2) Adhesive otitis media [scarring of ear drum] associated with hearing level by audiometric test of 20 db or more average for the speech frequencies (500, 1000, and 2000 cycles per second) in either ear regardless of the hearing level in the other ear.

(3) Acute or chronic serous otitis media [fluid-producing middle-ear infection].

(4) Presence of attic [area in middle ear] perforation in which presence of cholesteatoma [cholesterol tumor] is suspected.

(5) Repeated attacks of catarrhal otitis media [middle ear inflammation]; intact grayish thickened drum(s).

f. Tympanic membrane [ear drum].

(1) Any perforation of the tympanic membrane.

(2) Severe scarring of the tympanic membrane associated with hearing level by audiometric test of 20 db or more average for the speech frequencies (500, 1000, and 2000 cycles per second) in either ear regardless of the hearing level in the other ear.

g. Other diseases and defects of the ear which

obviously preclude satisfactory performance of duty or which require frequent and prolonged treatment.

2-7. Hearing (See also paragraph 2-6.)   The cause for rejection for appointment, enlistment, and induction is:

Hearing acuity level by audiometric testing (regardless of conversational or whispered voice hearing acuity) greater than that [described in the table below]. There is no objection to conducting the whispered voice test or the spoken voice test as a preliminary to conducting the audiometric hearing test.

Acceptable Audiometric Hearing Level (Present American Standard) for Appointment, Enlistment, and Induction

	250	500	1000	2000	3000	4000	6000	8000
	256	512	1024	2048	2896	4096	6144	8192
a. Both ears......	(1)	Average of the three (3) frequencies not greater than twenty (20) decibels with no level greater than twenty-five (25) decibels.			(2)	50	(2)	(1)
or								
b. Better ear........	(1)	15	15	15	(2)	30	(2)	(1)
Worse ear........	(1)	(1)	(1)	(1)	(1)	(1)	(1)	(1)

[1] No requirement.
[2] Not yet standardized.

SECTION VI. ENDOCRINE AND METABOLIC
DISORDERS

2-8. Endocrine and Metabolic Disorders   Th
causes for rejection for appointment, enlistment, an
induction are:

a. Adrenal gland, malfunction of, of any degree

b. Cretinism [thyroid hormone deficiency resultin
in low intellect and physical abnormalities].

c. Diabetes insipidus [deficiency of a pituitar
hormone with symptoms of excessive thirst an
urination].

d. Diabetes mellitus [insulin deficiency with symp
toms of high blood sugar and sugar in urine].

e. Gigantism or acromegaly [excess of a pituitar
growth hormone].

f. Glycosuria [sugar in urine], persistent, regard
less of cause.

g. Goiter.

   (1) Simple goiter [enlarged thyroid gland
with definite pressure symptoms or so large in siz
as to interfere with the wearing of a military uni
form or military equipment.

   (2) *Thyrotoxicosis* [excess of thyroid hor
mone].

h. Gout.

i. Hyperinsulinism [excessive insulin], confirmed
symptomatic.

j. Hyperparathyroidism [excessive calcium i
blood] and *hypoparathyroidism* [too little calciun
in blood].

k. Hypopituitarism [deficiency of pituitary hor
mones], severe.

l. Myxedema [thyroid hormone deficiency i
adults], spontaneous or postoperative (with clini

cal manifestations and not based solely on low
basal metabolic rate).

m. Nutritional deficiency diseases (including
sprue [chronic diarrhea], beriberi [vitamin B defi-
ciency], pellagra [vitamin B deficiency], and
scurvy [vitamin C deficiency]) which are more
than mild and not readily remediable or in which
permanent pathological changes have been established.

n. Other endocrine or metabolic disorders which
obviously preclude satisfactory performance of
military duty or which require frequent and prolonged treatment.

SECTION VII. EXTREMITIES

2-9. Upper Extremities (See paragraph 2-11.)
The causes for rejection for appointment, enlistment,
and induction are:

a. Limitation of motion. An individual will be
considered unacceptable if the joint ranges of
motion are less than the measurements listed below. [See chart printed in Appendix of this book.]

(1) *Shoulder.*

(*a*) Forward elevation to 90°.

(*b*) Abduction to 90°.

(2) *Elbow.*

(*a*) Flexion [bending] to 100°.

(*b*) Extension to 15°.

(3) *Wrist.* A total range of 15° (extension
plus flexion).

(4) *Hand.* Pronation [turning palm down]
to the first quarter of the normal arc. Supination
[turning palm up] to the first quarter of the normal arc.

(5) *Fingers*. Inability to clench fist, pick up a pin or needle, and grasp an object.

b. *Hand and fingers*.

(1) Absence (or loss) of more than one-third of the distal phalanx [part above joint] of either thumb.

(2) Absence (or loss) of distal and middle phalanx [part above second joint] of an index, middle, or ring finger of either hand irrespective of the absence (or loss) of little finger.

(2.1) Absence of more than the distal phalanx [part above first joint] of any two of the following fingers: index, middle, or ring finger of either hand.

(3) Absence of hand or any portion thereof except for fingers as noted above.

(4) Hyperdactylia [more than five fingers].

(5) Scars and deformities of the fingers and/or hand which impair circulation, are symptomatic, are so disfiguring as to make the individual objectionable in ordinary social relationships, or which impair normal function to such a degree as to interfere with the satisfactory performance of military duty.

c. *Wrist, forearm, elbow, arm, and shoulder*. Healed disease or injury of wrist, elbow, or shoulder with residual [lingering] weakness or symptoms of such a degree as to preclude satisfactory performance of duty.

2-10. Lower Extremities (See paragraph 2-11.) The causes for rejection for appointment, enlistment, and induction are:

a. *Limitation of motion*. An individual will be considered unacceptable if the joint ranges of motion are less than the measurements listed below. [See chart in Appendix.]

(1) *Hip*.
(a) Flexion [bending] to 90°.
(b) Extension to 10° (beyond 0).

(2) *Knee*.
(a) Full extension.
(b) Flexion to 90°.

(3) *Ankle*.
(a) Dorsiflexion [bending up] to 10°.
(b) Plantar flexion [bending down] to 10°.

(4) *Toes*. Stiffness which interferes with walking, marching, running, or jumping.

b. *Foot and ankle*.

(1) Absence of one or more small toes of one or both feet, if function of the foot is poor or running or jumping is precluded, or absence of foot or any portion thereof except for toes as noted herein.

(2) Absence (or loss) of great toe(s) or loss of dorsal flexion [ability to bend up] thereof if function of foot is impaired.

(3) Claw toes [clawlike distortion of toes] precluding the wearing of combat service boots.

(4) Clubfoot.

(5) Flatfoot, pronounced cases, with decided eversion [turning outward] of the foot and marked bulging of the inner border, due to the inward rotation of the astragalus [ball of ankle], regardless of the presence or absence of other symptoms.

(6) Flatfoot, spastic [painful muscle contraction causing flatfoot].

(7) Hallux valgus [curving of big toe over other toes], if severe and associated with marked exostosis or bunion.

(8) Hammer toe [hammerlike distortion of toe] which interferes with the wearing of combat service boots.

(9) Healed disease, injury or deformity including hyperdactylia [extra toes] which precludes running, is accompanied by disabling pain, or which prohibits the wearing of combat service boots.

(10) Ingrowing toenails, if severe and not remediable.

(11) Obliteration of the transverse arch associated with permanent flexion of the small toes.

(12) Pes cavus [opposite of flatfoot—exaggerated arch], with contracted plantar fascia, dorsiflexed toes, tenderness under the metatarsal heads, and callosity under the weight-bearing areas.

c. Leg, knee, thigh, and hip.

(1) Dislocated semilunar cartilage, loose or foreign bodies within the knee joint, or history of surgical correction of same if

(*a*) Within the preceding six months.

(*b*) Six months or more have elapsed since operation without recurrence, and there is instability of the knee ligaments in lateral or anteroposterior directions in comparison with the normal knee or abnormalities noted on X ray, there is significant atrophy or weakness of the thigh musculature in comparison with the normal side, there is not acceptable active motion in flexion and extension, or there are other symptoms of internal derangement.

(2) Authentic history or physical findings of an unstable or internally deranged joint causing disabling pain or seriously limiting function. Individuals with verified episodes of buckling or locking of the knee who have not undergone satisfactory surgical correction or if, subsequent to surgery, there is evidence of more than mild instability of the knee ligaments in lateral and anteroposterior directions in comparison with the normal knee, weakness or atrophy of the thigh musculature in comparison with the normal side, or if the individual requires medical treatment of sufficient frequency to interfere with the performance of military duty.

d. General.

(1) Deformities of one or both lower extremities which have interfered with function to such a degree as to prevent the individual from following a *physically active* vocation in civilian life or which would interfere with the satisfactory completion of prescribed training and performance of military duty.

(2) Diseases or deformities of the hip, knee, or ankle joint which interfere with walking, running, or weight bearing.

(3) Pain in the lower back or leg which is intractable and disabling to the degree of interfering with walking, running, and weight bearing.

(4) Shortening of a lower extremity resulting in any limp of noticeable degree.

2-11. Miscellaneous (See also paragraphs 2-9 and 2-10.)   The causes for rejection for enlistment, appointment, and induction are:

a. Arthritis [joint inflammation].

(1) Active or subacute arthritis, including Marie-Strumpell type [spinal arthritis].

(2) Chronic osteoarthritis or traumatic [caused by injury] arthritis of isolated joints of more than minimal degree, which has interfered with the following of a physically active vocation in civilian life or which precludes the satisfactory performance of military duty.

(3) Documented clinical history of rheumatoid arthritis.

(4) Traumatic arthritis of a major joint of more than minimal degree.

b. Disease of any bone or joint, healed, with such resulting deformity or rigidity that function is impaired to such a degree that it will interfere with military service.

c. Dislocation, old unreduced; substantiated history of recurrent dislocations of major joints; instability of a major joint, symptomatic and more than mild; or if, subsequent to surgery, there is evidence of more than mild instability in comparison with the normal joint, weakness or atrophy in comparison with the normal side, or if the individual requires medical treatment of sufficient frequency to interfere with the performance of military duty.

d. Fractures.

(1) Malunited [improperly healed] fractures that interfere significantly with function.

(2) Ununited fractures.

(3) Any old or recent fracture in which a plate, pin, or screws were used for fixation and left in place and which may be subject to easy trauma, i.e., as a plate tibia, etc.

e. Injury of a bone or joint within the preceding six weeks, without fracture or dislocation, of more than a minor nature.

f. Muscular paralysis, contracture, or atrophy, if progressive or of sufficient degree to interfere with military service.

f.1 Myotonia congenita [hereditary muscle disorder]. Confirmed.

g. Osteomyelitis [bone infection], active or recurrent, of any bone or bones or substantiated history of osteomyelitis of any of the long bones unless successfully treated two or more years previously without subsequent recurrence or disqualifying sequelae as demonstrated by both clinical and X-ray evidence.

h. Osteoporosis [thin or brittle bones].

i. Scars, extensive, deep, or adherent, of the skin and soft tissues or neuromas [nerve tumors] of an extremity which are painful, which interfere with muscular movements, which preclude the wearing of military equipment, or that show a tendency to break down.

j. Chondromalacia [softening of cartilage], manifested by verified history of joint effusion, interference with function, or residuals from surgery.

SECTION VIII. EYES AND VISION

2-12. Eyes   The causes for rejection for appointment, enlistment, and induction are:

a. Lids.

(1) Blepharitis [inflammation of lid ends], chronic more than mild. Cases of acute blepharitis will be rejected until cured.

(2) Blepharospasm [muscle spasm of eyelid].

(3) Dacryocystitis [tearduct infection], acute or chronic.

(4) Destruction of the lids, complete or extensive, sufficient to impair protection of the eye from exposure.

(5) Disfiguring cicatrices [scars] and adhesions of the eyelids to each other or to the eyeball.

(6) Growth or tumor of the eyelid other than small early basal cell tumors of the eyelid, which can be cured by treatment, and small nonprogressive asymptomatic benign lesions. (See also paragraphs 2-40 and 2-41.)

(7) Marked inversion [turning in] or eversion [turning out] of the eyelids sufficient to cause unsightly appearance or watering of eyes (entropion or ectropion).

(8) Lagophthalmos [inability to close lids].

(9) Ptosis [drooping of lid] interfering with vision.

(10) Trichiasis [eyelashes turning in toward eye], severe.

b. *Conjunctiva.*

(1) Conjunctivitis [inflammation of eye], chronic, including vernal catarrh and trachoma [viral eye infection]. Individuals with acute conjunctivitis are unacceptable until the condition is cured.

(2) Pterygium [membranous growth covering eyeball].

(*a*) Pterygium recurring after three operative procedures.

(*b*) Pterygium encroaching on the cornea in excess of 3 millimeters or interfering with vision.

c. Cornea.

(1) Dystrophy, corneal [hereditary opaque deposits in cornea], of any type including keratoconus [thinning of cornea] of any degree.

(2) Keratitis [inflammation of cornea], acute or chronic.

(3) Ulcer, corneal; history of recurrent ulcers or corneal abrasions (including herpetic [viral type] ulcers).

(4) Vascularization [growth of blood vessels into cornea] or opacification of the cornea from any cause which interferes with visual function or is progressive.

d. Uveal tract [iris and one layer of the eye]. Inflammation of the uveal tract except healed traumatic choroiditis.

e. Retina.

(1) Angiomatoses [blood vessel tumors], phakomatoses [small tumors in retina], retinal cysts [growths], and other congenito-hereditary conditions that impair visual function.

(2) Degenerations of the retina to include macular cysts, holes, and other degenerations (hereditary or acquired degenerative changes) and other conditions affecting the macula [part of the retina]. All types of pigmentary degenerations (primary and secondary).

(3) Detachment of the retina or history of surgery for same.

(4) Inflammation of the retina (retinitis or other inflammatory conditions of the retina to include Coat's disease, diabetic retinopathy, Eales' disease, and retinitis proliferans [scarring]).

f. Optic nerve.

(1) Congenito-hereditary conditions of the optic nerve or any other central nervous system pathology affecting the efficient function of the optic nerve.

(2) Optic neuritis [inflammation of optic nerve], neuroretinitis, or secondary optic atrophy resulting therefrom or documented history of attacks of retrobulbar neuritis [inflammation of optic nerve and tissues behind eyeball].

(3) Optic atrophy (primary or secondary) [degeneration of optic nerve].

(4) Papilledema [increase in pressure behind eye].

g. Lens.

(1) Aphakia (unilateral or bilateral) [absence of lens].

(2) Dislocation, partial or complete, of a lens.

(3) Opacities of the lens which interfere with vision or which are considered to be progressive.

h. Ocular mobility and motility.

(1) Diplopia [double vision], documented, constant or intermittent from any cause or of any degree interfering with visual function (i.e., may suppress).

(2) Diplopia, monocular [double vision in one eye], documented, interfering with visual function.

(3) Nystagmus [continuous involuntary movement of eyeballs when fixing on an object], with both eyes fixing, congenital or acquired.

(4) Strabismus [cross eyes] of 40 prism diopters or more, uncorrectable by lens to less than 40 diopters.

(5) Strabismus [cross eyes] of any degree accompanied by documented diplopia [double vision].

(6) Strabismus, surgery for the correction of, within the preceding six months.

i. Miscellaneous defects and diseases.

(1) Abnormal conditions of the eye or visual fields due to disease of the central nervous system.

(2) Absence of an eye.

(3) Asthenopia, severe [weakness or speedy tiring of eyes].

(4) Exophthalmos [protrusion of eyeball], unilateral or bilateral.

(5) Glaucoma [increased pressure within the eye], primary or secondary.

(6) Hemianopsia [one-half field vision] of any type.

(7) Loss of normal pupillary reflex reactions to light or accommodation to distance or Adie's syndrome.

(8) Loss of visual fields due to organic disease.

(9) Night blindness associated with objective disease of the eye. Verified congenital night blindness.

(10) Residuals of old contusions, lacerations, penetrations, etc., which impair visual function required for satisfactory performance of military duty.

(11) Retained intra-ocular foreign body.

(12) Tumors. See *a*(6) above and paragraphs 2-40 and 2-41.

(13) Any organic disease of the eye or adnexa [associated parts, e.g., lids, tear ducts, etc.] not specified above which threatens continuity of vision or impairment of visual function.

2-13. Vision   The causes for medical rejection for appointment, enlistment, and induction are:

a. Distant visual acuity. Distant visual acuity of any degree which does not correct to at least one of the following:

(1) 20/40 in one eye and 20/70 in the other eye.

(2) 20/30 in one eye and 20/100 in the other eye.

(3) 20/20 in one eye and 20/400 in the other eye.

b. Near visual acuity. Near visual acuity of any degree which does not correct to at least J–6 in the better eye.

c. Refractive error. Any degree of refractive error in spherical equivalent of over −8.00 or +8.00; or if ordinary spectacles cause discomfort by reason of ghost images, prismatic displacement, etc.; or if an ophthalmological consultation reveals a condition which is disqualifying.

d. Contact lens. Complicated cases requiring contact lens for adequate correction of vision such as keratoconus [thinning of cornea], corneal scars, and irregular astigmatism [irregular curvature of the cornea].

SECTION IX. GENITOURINARY SYSTEM*

2-14. Genitalia (See also paragraphs 2-40 and 2-41.)   The causes for rejection for appointment, enlistment, and induction are:

e. Hermaphroditism.

m. Testicle(s). (See also paragraphs 2-40 and 2-41.)

* The omitted items refer to women.

(1) Absence or nondescent of both testicles.

(2) Undiagnosed mass or enlargement of testicle or epididymis [part of the sperm duct].

(3) Undescended testicle.

q. Varicocele [enlarged veins around testicle] *or hydrocele* [fluid around testicle], if large or painful.

s. Major abnormalities and defects of the genitalia such as a change of sex, a history thereof, or complications (adhesions, disfiguring scars, etc.) residual to surgical correction of these conditions.

2-15. Urinary System (See paragraphs 2-8, 2-40, and 2-41.)   The causes for rejection for appointment, enlistment, and induction are:

a. Albuminuria [protein in urine] if persistent or recurrent including so-called orthostatic [caused by standing for a long time] or functional albuminuria.

b. Cystitis [bladder infection], *chronic*. Individuals with acute cystitis are unacceptable until the condition is cured.

c. Enuresis [inability to hold back urine; bedwetting] determined to be a symptom of an organic defect not amenable to treatment. (See also paragraph 2-34*c* [Chapter Four].)

d. Epispadias or hypospadias [opening of penis on top or bottom] when accompanied by evidence of infection of the urinary tract or if clothing is soiled when voiding.

e. Hematuria [blood in urine], *cylindruria* [abnormal finding in urine due to kidney disease], or other findings indicative of renal tract disease [kidney disease].

f. Incontinence of urine [involuntary urination].

g. Kidney.

(1) Absence of one kidney, regardless of cause.

(2) Acute or chronic infections of the kidney.

(3) Cystic [having a cavity] or polycystic [having multiple cavities] kidney, confirmed history of.

(4) Hydronephrosis [blockage of urinary tract] or pyonephrosis [infected blockage of urinary tract].

(5) Nephritis, acute or chronic [inflammation of kidney].

(6) Pyelitis, pyelonephritis [infection of kidney].

h. Penis, amputation of, if the resulting stump is insufficient to permit micturition in a normal manner.

i. Peyronie's disease [hardening of tissues in penis causing painful erection].

j. Prostate gland, hypertrophy [enlargement] of, with urinary retention.

k. Renal calculus [kidney stone].

(1) Substantiated history of bilateral renal calculus at any time.

(2) Verified history of renal calculus at any time with evidence of stone formation within the preceding twelve months, current symptoms or positive X ray for calculus.

m. Urethra.

(1) Stricture [narrowing] of the urethra.

(2) Urethritis [infection of urethra], acute or chronic, other than gonorrheal urethritis without complications.

n. Urinary fistula [perforation in urinary tract].

o. Other diseases and defects of the urinary system which obviously preclude satisfactory performance of duty or which require frequent and prolonged treatment.

SECTION X. HEAD AND NECK

2-16. Head   The causes for rejection for appointment, enlistment, and induction are:

a. Abnormalities which are apparently temporary in character resulting from recent injuries until a period of three months has elapsed. These include severe contusions and other wounds of the scalp and cerebral concussion. See paragraph 2-31.

b. Deformities of the skull in the nature of depressions, exostoses [bony tumors], etc., of a degree which would prevent the individual from wearing a gas mask or military headgear.

c. Deformities of the skull of any degree associated with evidence of disease of the brain, spinal cord, or peripheral nerves.

d. Depressed fractures near the central sulcus [main groove in brain] with or without convulsive seizures.

e. Loss or congenital absence of the bony structure of the skull not successfully corrected by reconstructive material:

(1) All cases involving absence of the bony substance of the skull which have been corrected but in which the defect is in excess of 1 square inch or the size of a 25-cent piece, will be referred to the Surgeon General with a report of consultation;

(2) The report of consultation will include an evaluation of any evidence of alteration of

brain function in any of its several spheres, i.e.,
intelligence, judgment, perception, behavior, motor
control, and sensory function as well as any evidence of active bone disease or other related complications. Current X rays and other pertinent
laboratory data will accompany such a report of
consultation.

f. Unsightly deformities, such as large birthmarks,
large hairy moles, extensive scars, and mutilations
due to injuries or surgical operations; ulcerations;
fistulae [perforations], atrophy, or paralysis of
part of the face or head.

2-17. Neck The causes for rejection for appointment, enlistment, and induction are:

a. Cervical ribs [extra pair of ribs in neck] if
symptomatic, or so obvious that they are found
on routine physical examination. (Detection based
primarily on X ray is not considered to meet this
criterion.)

b. Congenital cysts [growths filled with fluid] of
branchial cleft origin or those developing from the
remnants of the thyroglossal duct, with or without
fistulous tracts [openings to the outside].

c. Fistula, chronic draining, of any type [opening
to the outside which drains fluid].

d. [Deleted.]

e. Nonspastic contraction [shortening] of the
muscles of the neck or cicatricial [muscle scar]
contracture of the neck to the extent that it interferes with the wearing of a uniform or military
equipment or is so disfiguring as to make the individual objectionable in common social relationships.

f. Spastic contraction of the muscles of the neck, persistent and chronic.

g. Tumor of thyroid or other structures of the neck. See paragraphs 2-40 and 2-41.

Section XI. Heart and Vascular System

2-18. Heart   The causes for rejection for appointment, enlistment, and induction are:

a. All organic valvular diseases of the heart, including those improved by surgical procedures.

b. Coronary artery disease or myocardial infarction [conventional heart attack involving permanent scarring], old or recent or true angina pectoris [chest pain related to exertion], at any time.

c. Electrocardiographic evidence of major arrhythmias [abnormal heartbeat] such as:

(1) Atrial tachycardia [rapid heartbeat], flutter, or fibrillation, ventricular tachycardia or fibrillation.

(2) Conduction defects such as first degree atrioventricular block and right bundle branch block. (These conditions occurring as isolated findings are not unfitting when cardiac evaluation reveals no cardiac disease.)

(3) Left bundle branch block, second and third degree AV block.

(4) Unequivocal electrocardiographic evidence of old or recent myocardial infarction [heart attack]; coronary insufficiency [insufficient blood supply to heart] at rest or after stress; or evidence of heart muscle disease.

d. Hypertrophy or dilatation of the heart [enlarged heart] as evidenced by clinical examination or roentgenographic examination [X ray] and supported by electrocardiographic examination. Care should be taken to distinguish abnormal enlargement from increased diastolic filling as seen in the well conditioned subject [an athlete, for instance] with a sinus bradycardia [normal slow heartbeat]. Cases of enlarged heart by X ray not supported by electrocardiographic examination will be forwarded to the Surgeon General for evaluation.

e. Myocardial insufficiency [inability of heart to pump blood normally] (congestive circulatory failure, cardiac decompensation) obvious or covert, regardless of cause.

f. Paroxysmal tachycardia [intermittently rapid heartbeat] within the previous five years, or at any time if recurrent or disabling or if associated with evidence of accelerated AV conduction (Wolff-Parkinson-White).

g. Pericarditis [inflammation around the heart]; *endocarditis* [inflammation of heart lining]; *or myocarditis* [inflammation of heart muscle], history or finding of, except for a history of a single acute idiopathic [of unknown cause] or coxsackie [type of virus] pericarditis with no residuals, or tuberculosis pericarditis adequately treated with no residuals and inactive for 2 years.

h. Tachycardia persistent with a resting pulse rate of 100 or more, regardless of cause.

2-19. Vascular System [blood vessels]   The causes for rejection for appointment, enlistment, and induction are:

a. Congenital or acquired lesions of the aorta and major vessels, such as syphilitic aortitis, demonstrable atherosclerosis [hardening of the arteries] which interferes with circulation, congenital or acquired dilatation of the aorta (especially if associated with the other features of Marfan's syndrome), and pronounced dilatation of the main pulmonary artery.

b. Hypertension evidenced by preponderant blood pressure readings of 150–mm or more systolic in an individual over thirty-five years of age or preponderant readings of 140–mm or more systolic in an individual thirty-five years of age or less. Preponderant diastolic pressure over 90–mm diastolic is cause for rejection at any age.

c. Marked circulatory instability as indicated by orthostatic hypotension [drop in blood pressure upon standing up], persistent tachycardia [rapid heartbeat], severe peripheral vasomotor disturbances, and sympatheticotonia [tension-induced rise in blood pressure].

d. Peripheral vascular disease [disease of small blood vessels] including Raynaud's phenomena, Buerger's disease (thromboangiitis obliterans), erythromelalgia, arteriosclerotic and diabetic vascular diseases. Special tests will be employed in doubtful cases.

e. Thrombophlebitis [clots in veins].

(1) History of thrombophlebitis with persistent thrombus [clot] or evidence of circulatory obstruction or deep venous incompetence [inability of blood to return from lower extremities] in the involved veins.

(2) Recurrent thrombophlebitis.

f. Varicose veins [enlarged veins], if more than mild, or if associated with edema [swelling], skin ulceration, or residual scars from ulceration.

2-20. Miscellaneous The causes for rejection for appointment, enlistment, and induction are:

a. Aneurysm [ballooning of a section] *of the heart or major vessel,* congenital or acquired.

b. History and evidence of a congenital abnormality which has been treated by surgery but with residual abnormalities or complications, *for example*: Patent ductus arteriosus [abnormal connection between pulmonary artery and aorta] with residual cardiac enlargement or pulmonary hypertension [increased pressure in pulmonary artery]; resection of a coarctation [narrowing] of the aorta without a graft when there are other cardiac abnormalities or complications; closure of a secundum type atrial septal defect [hole in the wall between the upper chambers of the heart] when there are residual abnormalities or complications.

c. Major congenital abnormalities and defects of the heart and vessels unless satisfactorily corrected without residuals or complications. Uncomplicated dextrocardia [heart on right side instead of left] and other minor asymptomatic anomalies are acceptable.

d. Substantiated history of rheumatic fever or chorea [abnormal and uncontrolled motion of parts of body] within the previous two years, recurrent attacks of rheumatic fever or chorea at any time, or with evidence of residual cardiac damage.

SECTION XII. HEIGHT, WEIGHT, AND BODY BUILD

2-21. Height The causes for rejection for appointment, enlistment, and induction are:

b. For enlistments and induction.

(1) *Men.* Height below 60 inches or over 80 inches for Army and Air Force.

(2) *Men.* Height below 60 inches and over 78 inches for Navy and Marine Corps.

2-22. Weight   The causes for rejection for appointment, enlistment, and induction are:

a. *Weight related to height* which is below the minimum [shown in the table on page 46].

b. *Weight related to age and height* which is in excess of the maximum [shown in the table on page 46].

2-23. Body Build   The causes for rejection for appointment, enlistment, and induction are:

a. *Congenital malformation of bones and joints.* (See paragraphs 2-9, 2-10, and 2-11.)

b. *Deficient muscular development* which would interfere with the completion of required training.

c. *Evidences of congenital asthenia*: slender bones; weak thorax; visceroptosis [drooping internal organs]; severe, chronic constipation; or "drop heart" if marked in degree.

d. *Obesity.* Even though the individual's weight is within the maximum [shown in the Tables of Weight], he will be reported as medically unacceptable when the medical examiner considers that the individual's weight in relation to the bony structure and musculature constitutes obesity of such a degree as to interfere with the satisfactory completion of prescribed training.

SECTION XIII. LUNGS AND CHEST WALL

2-24. General   The following conditions are causes for rejection for appointment, enlistment, and

TABLES OF WEIGHT

Table of Militarily Acceptable Weight
(in Pounds) as Related to Age and Height
for Males—Initial Procurement

Height (inches)	Minimum (regardless of age)	Maximum					
		16–20 years	21–24 years	25–30 years	31–35 years	36–40 years	41 years and over
60.........	100	163	173	173	173	168	164
61.........	102	171	176	175	175	171	166
62.........	103	174	178	178	177	173	169
63.........	104	178	182	181	180	176	171
64.........	105	183	184	185	185	180	175
65.........	106	187	190	191	190	185	180
66.........	107	191	196	197	196	190	185
67.........	111	196	201	202	201	195	190
68.........	115	202	207	208	207	201	195
69.........	119	208	213	214	212	206	200
70.........	123	214	219	219	218	211	205
71.........	127	219	224	225	223	216	210
72.........	131	225	231	232	230	224	216
73.........	135	231	239	238	237	230	223
74.........	139	237	246	246	243	236	229
75.........	143	243	253	253	251	243	235
76.........	147	248	260	260	257	250	241
77.........	151	254	267	267	264	256	248
78.........	153	260	275	273	271	263	254
★*79.........	159	266	281	279	277	269	260
★*80.........	166	273	288	286	284	276	267

★* Applies only to personnel enlisted, inducted or appointed in Army and enlisted or inducted into Air Force. Does not apply to Navy or Marine Corps enlistees or inductees.

induction until further study indicates recovery without disqualifying sequelae:

a. Abnormal elevation of the diaphragm on either side.

b. Acute abscess of the lung.

c. Acute bronchitis until the condition is cured.

d. Acute fibrinous pleurisy [inflammation of lining of lung]. associated with acute nontuberculous pulmonary infection.

e. Acute mycotic disease [fungus infection] of the lung such as coccidioidomycosis and histoplasmosis.

f. Acute nontuberculous pneumonia.

g. Foreign body in trachea or bronchus.

h. Foreign body of the chest wall causing symptoms.

i. Lobectomy [removal of part of the lung], history of, for a nontuberculous nonmalignant lesion with residual pulmonary disease. Removal of more than one lobe is cause for rejection regardless of the absence of residuals.

j. Other traumatic lesions of the chest or its contents.

k. Pneumothorax [partial or complete collapse of lung], or history thereof, within one year of date of examination if due to simple trauma or surgery; within three years of date of examination if of spontaneous origin. Surgical correction is acceptable if no significant residuals, disease, or deformity remains and pulmonary function tests are within normal limits.

l. Recent fracture of ribs, sternum [breast bone], clavicle [collar bone], or scapula [shoulder blade].

m. Significant abnormal findings on physical examination of the chest.

2-25. Tuberculous Lesions (See also paragraph 2-38.)   The causes for rejection for appointment, enlistment, and induction are:

a. Active tuberculosis in any form or location.

b. Pulmonary tuberculosis, active within the previous two years.

c. Substantiated history of one or more reactivations or relapses of pulmonary tuberculosis or other definite evidence of poor host resistance to the tubercle bacillus.

2-26. Nontuberculous Lesions The causes for rejection for appointment, enlistment, and induction are:

b. Bronchial asthma, except for childhood asthma with a trustworthy history of freedom from symptoms since the twelfth birthday.

c. Bronchitis, chronic with evidence of pulmonary function disturbance.

d. Bronchiectasis [chronic and localized type of bronchial infection].

e. Bronchopleural fistula [abnormal type of connection in lung].

f. Bullous or generalized pulmonary emphysema [respiratory disease].

g. Chronic abscess of lung.

h. Chronic fibrous pleuritis [inflammation of lining of lung] of sufficient extent to interfere with pulmonary function or obscure the lung field in the roentgenogram.

i. Chronic mycotic [fungus] *diseases* of the lung including coccidioidomycosis; residual cavitation or more than a few small-sized inactive and stable residual nodules demonstrated to be due to mycotic disease.

j. Empyema [infection of lung lining], residual sacculation or unhealed sinuses [perforations] of chest wall following operation for empyema.

k. Extensive pulmonary fibrosis [scarring] from any cause, producing dyspnea [shortness of breath] on exertion.

l. Foreign body of the lung or mediastinum [space between the lungs] causing symptoms or active inflammatory reaction.

m. Multiple cystic disease [cavities of lung] of the lung or solitary cyst which is large and incapacitating.

o. Osteomyelitis [bone infection] of rib, sternum, clavicle, scapula, or vertebra.

p. Pleurisy with effusion [water on the lung] of unknown origin within the previous two years.

q. Sarcoidosis [disease affecting lungs and lymph nodes]. See paragraph 2-38.

r. Suppurative periostitis [pus-producing infection around bones] of rib, sternum, clavicle, scapula, or vertebra.

SECTION XIV. MOUTH, NOSE, PHARYNX, TRACHEA, ESOPHAGUS, AND LARYNX

2-27. Mouth   The causes for rejection for appointment, enlistment, and induction are:

a. Hard palate, perforation of.

b. Harelip, unless satisfactorily repaired by surgery.

c. Leukoplakia, if severe [white thickening of part of mouth].

d. Lips, unsightly mutilations of, from wounds, burns, or disease.

e. Ranula [tumor on underside of tongue], if extensive. For other tumors see paragraphs 2-40 and 2-41.

2-28. Nose   The causes for rejection for appointment, enlistment, and induction are:

a. Allergic manifestations.

(1) Chronic atrophic rhinitis [inflammation of nasal membranes].

(2) Hay fever if severe and if not controllable by antihistamines or by desensitization, or both.

b. Choana, atresia, or stenosis of [absence, closure, or narrowing of the connection between nose and throat], if symptomatic.

c. Nasal septum, perforation of:

(1) Associated with interference of function, ulceration of crusting, and when the result of organic disease.

(2) If progressive.

(3) If respiration is accompanied by a whistling sound.

d. Sinusitis, acute [inflammation of sinuses].

e. Sinusitis, chronic, when more than mild.

(1) Evidenced by any of the following: chronic purulent nasal discharge, large nasal polyps [growths], hyperplastic changes [thickening] of the nasal tissues, or symptoms requiring frequent medical attention.

(2) Confirmed by transillumination or X-ray examination or both.

2-29. Pharynx, Trachea, Esophagus, and Larynx
The causes for rejection for appointment, enlistment, and induction are:

a. Esophagus, organic disease of, such as ulceration, varices [enlarged veins], achalasia [enlargement of esophagus]; peptic esophagitis [inflammation of esophagus]; if confirmed by appropriate X-ray or esophagoscopic examinations.

b. Laryngeal [voice box] *paralysis,* sensory or motor, due to any cause.

c. Larynx, organic disease of, such as neoplasm [cancer], polyps [growths], granuloma [scar tissue tumor], ulceration, and chronic laryngitis.

d. Plica dysphonia ventricularis [abnormal voice due to malfunction of vocal cords].

e. Tracheostomy [operation resulting in hole in trachea] *or tracheal fistula* [persistent perforation].

2-30. Other Defects and Diseases   The causes for appointment, enlistment, and induction are:

a. Aphonia [loss of voice].

b. Deformities or conditions of the mouth, throat, pharynx, larynx, esophagus, and nose which interfere with mastication and swallowing of ordinary food, with speech, or with breathing.

c. Destructive syphilitic disease of the mouth, nose, throat, larynx, or esophagus. (See paragraph 2-42.)

d. Pharyngitis [sore throat] *and nasopharyngitis* [inflamed nose and throat], chronic with positive history and objective evidence, if of such a degree as to result in excessive time lost in the military environment.

SECTION XV. NEUROLOGICAL DISORDERS

2-31. Neurological Disorders   The causes for rejection for appointment, enlistment, and induction are:

a. Degenerative disorders.

(1) Cerebellar and Friedreich's ataxia [degeneration of part of brain].

(2) Cerebral arteriosclerosis [hardening of arteries in brain].

(3) Encephalomyelitis [inflammation of brain], residuals of, which preclude the satisfactory performance of military duty.

(4) Huntington's chorea [inherited disorder of central nervous system].

(5) Multiple sclerosis.

(6) Muscular atrophies [degeneration] and dystrophies of any type.

b. Miscellaneous.

(1) Congenital malformations if associated with neurological manifestations and meningocele [protrusion of covering of brain] even if uncomplicated.

(2) Migraine when frequent and incapacitating.

(3) Paralysis or weakness, deformity, discoordination, pain, sensory disturbance, intellectual deficit, disturbances of consciousness, or personality abnormalities regardless of cause which are of such a nature or degree as to preclude the satisfactory performance of military duty.

(4) Tremors, spasmodic torticollis [wry neck], athetosis [slow, involuntary writhing, especially of hands], or other abnormal movements more than mild.

c. Neurosyphilis of any form (general paresis, tabes dorsalis, meningovascular syphilis).

d. Paroxysmal [intermittent] *convulsive disorders,* disturbances of consciousness, all forms of psychomotor or temporal lobe epilepsy or history thereof except for seizures associated with toxic states or fever during childhood up to the age of twelve.

e. Peripheral nerve disorder.

(1) Polyneuritis [inflammation of nerves].

(2) Mononeuritis [inflammation of one nerve] or neuralgia [intermittent pain along course of nerve] which is chronic or recurrent and of an intensity that is periodically incapacitating.

(3) Neurofibromatosis [multiple nerve tumors on surface of skin].

f. Spontaneous subarachnoid hemorrhage [brain hemorrhage], verified history of, unless cause has been surgically corrected.

[Section XVI (including subsections 2-32 through 2-34) on psychiatric disorders is reprinted in Chapter Four of this book.]

SECTION XVII. SKIN AND CELLULAR TISSUES

2-35. Skin and Cellular Tissues   The causes for rejection for appointment, enlistment, and induction are:

a. Acne, severe, when the face is markedly disfigured or when extensive involvement of the neck, shoulders, chest, or back would be aggravated by or interfere with the wearing of military equipment.

b. Atopic dermatitis [allergic skin disease]. With active or residual lesions in characteristic areas (face and neck, antecubital [inside of elbow] and popliteal fossae [inside of knee], occasionally wrists and hands), or documented history thereof.

c. Cysts.

(1) *Cysts, other than pilonidal* [between the buttocks]. Of such a size or location as to interfere with the normal wearing of military equipment.

(2) *Cysts, pilonidal* [between the buttocks].

Pilonidal cysts, if evidenced by the presence of a tumor mass or a discharging sinus.

d. Dermatitis factitia [artificially caused inflammation of the skin, either intentional or unintentional].

e. Dermatitis herpetiformis [viral skin disease].

f. Eczema. Any type which is chronic and resistant to treatment.

f.1 Elephantiasis or chronic lymphedema [swelling of extremities].

g. Epidermolysis bullosa; pemphigus [recurring groups of blisters on skin].

h. Fungus infections, systemic or superficial types: If extensive and not amenable to treatment.

i. Furunculosis [infection of hair follicles]. Extensive, recurrent, or chronic.

j. Hyperhidrosis [severe perspiration] of hands or feet: chronic or severe.

k. Ichthyosis [dry skin]. Severe.

l. Leprosy. Any type.

m. Leukemia cutis [leukemia of skin]; *mycosis fungoides* [fungus condition]; *Hodgkin's disease.*

n. Lichen planus [skin disease characterized by wide, flat growths].

o. Lupus erythematosus (acute, subacute, or chronic) or any other dermatosis aggravated by sunlight.

p. Neurofibromatosis [multiple nerve tumors on skin] (von Recklinghausen's disease).

q. Nevi [moles] *or vascular tumors*: if extensive, unsightly, or exposed to constant irritation.

r. Psoriasis or a verified history thereof.

s. Radiodermatitis [inflammation of skin due to radiation].

t. Scars which are so extensive, deep, or adherent

that they may interfere with the wearing of military equipment, or that show a tendency to ulcerate.

u. Scleroderma [thickening of skin]. Diffuse type.

v. Tuberculosis. See paragraph 2-38.

w. Urticaria [hives]. Chronic.

x. Warts, plantar [warts on soles of feet], which have materially interfered with the following of a useful vocation in civilian life.

y. Xanthoma [yellow cholesterol deposits on skin]. If disabling or accompanied by hypercholesterolemia [excess cholesterol in blood] or hyperlipemia [excess fatty acids in blood].

z. Any other chronic skin disorder of a degree or nature which requires frequent outpatient treatment or hospitalization, interferes with the satisfactory performance of duty, or is so disfiguring as to make the individual objectionable in ordinary social relationships.

aa. Tattoos on any part of the body which in the opinion of the examining physician are obscene or so extensive on exposed areas as to be considered unsightly, are administratively disqualifying.

SECTION XVIII. SPINE, SCAPULAE, RIBS, AND SACROILIAC JOINTS

2-36. Spine and Sacroiliac Joints (See also paragraph 2-11.)   The causes for rejection for appointment, enlistment, and induction are:

a. Arthritis. See paragraph 2-11*a*.

b. Complaint of disease or injury of the spine or sacroiliac joints either with or without objective signs and symptoms which have prevented the individual from successfully following a physically active vocation in civilian life. Substantiation or documentation of the complaint without symptoms and objective signs is required.

c. Deviation or curvature of the spine from normal alignment, structure, or function (scoliosis [to either side], kyphosis [outward], or lordosis [inward], spina bifida occulta [minor split in base of spine], spondylolysis [destruction of a vertebra], etc.), if—

(1) Mobility and weight-bearing power is poor.

(2) More than moderate restriction of normal physical activities is required.

(3) Of such a nature as to prevent the individual from following a *physically active vocation* in civilian life.

(4) Of a degree which will interfere with the wearing of a uniform or military equipment.

(5) Symptomatic, associated with positive physical findings demonstrable by X ray.

d. Diseases of the lumbosacral or sacroiliac joints of a chronic type and obviously associated with pain referred to the lower extremities, muscular spasm, postural deformities, and limitation of motion in the lumbar region of the spine.

e. Granulomatous diseases [inflammatory tumors] either active or healed.

f. Healed fracture of the spine or pelvic bones with associated symptoms that have prevented the individual from following a *physically* active vocation in civilian life or which preclude the satisfactory performance of military duty.

g. Ruptured nucleus pulposus (herniation of intervertebral disk) or history of operation for this condition.

h. Spondylolysis [destruction of a vertebra] *or spondylolisthesis* [slippage of a vertebra forward] that is symptomatic or is likely to interfere with performance of duty or is likely to require assignment limitations.

2-37. Scapulae, Clavicles, and Ribs (See also paragraph 2-11.)   The causes for rejection for appointment, enlistment, and induction are:

a. Fractures, until well healed, and until determined that the residuals thereof will not preclude the satisfactory performance of military duty.

b. Injury within the preceding six weeks, without fracture or dislocation, of more than a minor nature.

c. Osteomyelitis [bone infection] of rib, sternum, clavicle, scapula, or vertebra.

d. Prominent scapulae [shoulder blades] interfering with function or with wearing of uniform or military equipment.

SECTION XIX. SYSTEMIC DISEASES AND MISCELLANEOUS CONDITIONS AND DEFECTS

2-38. Systemic Diseases [diseases affecting many parts of body simultaneously]   The causes for rejection for appointment, enlistment, and induction are:

a. Dermatomyositis [inflammation of muscles and skin rash].

b. Lupus erythematosus; acute, subacute, or chronic.

c. Progressive systemic sclerosis [scarring].

d. Reiter's disease [symptoms: arthritis, inflammation of eye, urethral discharge].

e. Sarcoidosis [disease frequently confused with TB but of unknown cause].

f. Scleroderma [thickening of skin], diffuse type.

g. Tuberculosis.

(1) Active tuberculosis in any form or location or substantiated by a substantiated history, or a substantiated history of active tuberculosis within the previous two years.

(2) Substantiated history of one or more reactivations or relapses of tuberculosis in any form or location or other definite evidence of poor host resistance to the tubercle bacillus.

(3) Residual physical or mental defects from past tuberculosis that would preclude satisfactory performance of duty.

2-39. General and Miscellaneous Conditions and Defects The causes for rejection for appointment, enlistment, and induction are:

a. Allergic manifestations.

(1) Allergic rhinitis (hay fever). See paragraph 2-28.

(2) Asthma. See paragraph 2-26*b*.

(3) Allergic dermatoses [skin allergies]. See paragraph 2-35.

(4) Visceral, abdominal, and cerebral allergy, if severe or not responsive to treatment.

(5) Bonafide history of moderate or severe generalized (as opposed to local) allergic reaction to insect bites or stings. Bonafide history of severe generalized reaction to common foods, e.g., milk, eggs, beef, and pork.

b. Any acute pathological condition [severe disease], including acute communicable diseases, until recovery has occurred without sequelae.

c. Any deformity which is markedly unsightly or which impairs general functional ability to such an extent as to prevent satisfactory performance of military duty.

d. Chronic metallic poisoning especially beryllium, manganese, and mercury. Undesirable residuals from lead, arsenic, or silver poisoning make the examinee medically unacceptable.

e. Cold injury, residuals of (example: frostbite, chilblain, immersion foot, or trench foot), such as deep-seated ache, paresthesia [abnormal sensation], hyperhidrosis [excessive sweating], easily traumatized skin, cyanosis [blueness], amputation of any digit, or ankylosis [frozen joint].

f. Positive tests for syphilis with negative TPI test unless there is a documented history of adequately treated lues [syphilis] or any of the several conditions which are known to give a false-positive S.T.S. [blood test] (vaccinia, infectious hepatitis, immunizations, atypical pneumonia, etc.) or unless there has been a reversal to a negative S.T.S. during an appropriate follow-up period (three to six months).

g. Filariasis; trypanosomiasis; amebiasis; schistosomiasis [types of parasites], *uncinariasis* (hookworm) associated with anemia, malnutrition, etc., if more than mild, and other similar worm or animal parasitic infestations, including the carrier states thereof.

h. Heat pyrexia (heatstroke, sunstroke, etc.): documented evidence of predisposition (includes disorders of sweat mechanism and previous serious episode), recurrent episodes requiring medical attention, or residual injury resulting therefrom (especially cardiac, cerebral, hepatic, and renal).

i. Industrial solvent and other chemical intoxication, chronic, including carbon bisulfide, trichlorethylene, carbon tetrachloride, and methyl cellosolve.

j. Mycotic [fungus] *infection* of internal organs.

k. Myositis [inflammation of muscles] or *fibrositis* [inflammation of tissues]; severe, chronic.

l. Residuals of tropical fevers and various parasitic or protozoal infestations which in the opinion of the medical examiner preclude the satisfactory performance of military duty.

Section XX. Tumors and Malignant Diseases

2-40. Benign Tumors   The causes for rejection for appointment, enlistment, and induction are:

a. Any tumor of the

    (1) Auditory canal, if obstructive.

    (2) Eye or orbit. See also paragraph 2-12*a* (6).

    (3) Kidney, bladder, testicle, or penis.

    (4) Central nervous system and its membraneous coverings unless five years after surgery and no otherwise disqualifying residuals of surgery or of original lesion.

b. Benign tumors of the abdominal wall if sufficiently large to interfere with military duty.

c. Benign tumors of bone likely to continue to enlarge, be subjected to trauma during military service, or show malignant potential.

d. Benign tumors of the thyroid or other structures of the neck, including enlarged lymph nodes, if the enlargement is of such a degree as to interfere with the wearing of a uniform or military equipment.

e. Tongue, benign tumor of, if it interferes with function.

f. Breast, thoracic contents, or chest wall, tumors of, other than fibromata lipomata [fatty tumor], and inclusion or sebaceous cysts which do not interfere with military duty.

2-41. Malignant Diseases and Tumors   The causes for rejection for appointment, enlistment, and induction are:

a. Leukemia, acute or chronic.

b. Malignant lymphomata [tumor of lymph glands].

c. Malignant tumor of any kind, at any time, substantiated diagnosis of, even though surgically removed, confirmed by accepted laboratory procedures, except as noted in paragraph 2-12a(6).

SECTION XXI. VENEREAL DISEASES

2-42. Venereal Diseases   In general the finding of acute, uncomplicated venereal disease which can be expected to respond to treatment is not cause for medical rejection for military service. The causes for rejection for appointment, enlistment, and induction are:

a. Chronic venereal disease which has not satisfactorily responded to treatment. The finding of a positive serologic test for syphilis following the adequate treatment of syphilis is not in itself considered evidence of chronic venereal disease which has not responded to treatment (paragraph 2-39*f*).

b. Complications and permanent residuals of venereal disease if progressive, of such nature as to interfere with the satisfactory performance of military duty, or if subject to aggravation by military service.

c. Neurosyphilis. See paragraph 2-31*c*.

3

The Gray Area

SEVERAL MYSTERIOUS "MAYBE IT'S THERE, MAYBE
it isn't" maladies appear among the Army's listed
causes for rejection for military service.

Very real to their sufferers, these conditions completely elude detection by any objective tests. Doctors
and Army medical examiners must base their diagnoses solely on subjective observations and information offered by their patients.

Except for these elusive ailments, thousands would
have been soldiers who have remained civilians.

Other thousands of men, vigorously healthy by
their own admission, have been disqualified for military service because they *once* were sick. They discovered that the Armed Forces do not want anyone
who ever had a severe generalized allergic reaction to

milk, a moderate generalized reaction to a bee sting, or bronchial asthma any time after the age of twelve (AR 40-501, sec. 2-39).*

A doctor's testimony to one of these conditions (or to any of several other erstwhile ailments that are cause for rejection) is all that is needed to claim a I-Y.

The Army publication AR 40-501 attempts to standardize the criteria by which men will be evaluated so that every man may be judged fairly. But not even the United States Department of Defense is capable of cataloguing all "the thousand natural shocks that flesh is heir to." Introductory remarks to AR 40-501 state that the aim of the standards is to prevent the induction of anyone who has a defect which would be aggravated by military service or whose treatment would interfere with Army duties.

The Army included in its fitness standards certain statements which would admit many complaints not specifically listed as cause for disqualification. One such statement gives as cause for exemption: "pain . . . regardless of cause which is of such a nature or degree as to preclude the satisfactory performance of duty" (2-31*b*[3]). Because of such blanket clauses, disqualifications have been granted for surprising reasons.

A young man who required a daily shampoo for a scalp condition was recently classified I-Y at a Northeastern examining station. The Army could not guarantee that he would be able to wash his hair

* All disqualifying conditions mentioned in this chapter are cross referenced with the Army's standards printed in Chapter Two of this book.

daily; to avoid the possibility of aggravating his condition, they declined to draft him.

Just as an extremely itchy scalp resulted in an exemption, so, in at least one case, has chronic nightly insomnia requiring drugs for relief. Neither of these conditions is a listed cause for rejection, but both required daily treatment that might have been interrupted during military service.

Anyone with a condition requiring daily care has potential grounds for exemption, particularly if an interruption of treatment might aggravate the defect. Wanting neither to hinder treatment nor to assume responsibility for the results, the Army may well decide not to draft.

Although some of the Army's rulings on men's fitness seem based on reason, many others appear the result of an inequitable process of selection. Men are inducted who are unqualified, and those who have nothing wrong with them are frequently rejected. The explanation is not complex: because of its voracious appetite for soldiers, the Army is concerned with masses of men rather than with individuals. That some fit men escape the draft disturbs the Army little. Their escape in no way affects the number inducted from the vast pool of possible candidates. Far more upsetting to the military is that unfit men are inducted and become the Army's responsibility through the same flaws in the system.

"Even when we suspect malingering, to prove it is very difficult," admits Col. William G. Peard, head of the Army department which sets the medical standards for induction. "A registrant may play upon some defect which might be minor, and it's almost impossible for a physician to say he's lying."

It is not only very difficult for the Army to prove a registrant has exaggerated his problem—or has no problem at all—it is virtually impossible within the present setup. The military relies almost exclusively on the preinduction physical and the physical inspection given at the time of induction to screen out the unfit and to verify claimed defects.

But these examinations are gross and hurried reviews, likely to miss large defects as well as small ones. Sometimes, as if they did not trust their own judgment, Army examiners may even ask a registrant to obtain civilian verification of an obvious and incapacitating flaw.

Only when fakery is flagrant or in categories where the need for men is critical (as it is for doctors and dentists) is any detective-type investigation of a registrant's claimed defect undertaken.

Colonel Peard concedes that under these conditions, collusion between registrants and civilian doctors probably exists. But, he says, the Army elects to simply trust the doctors. Unless the military wishes to devote resources to large-scale investigations, they have no other choice.

Because the Army's physicals are so haphazard and inefficient, and because investigations are virtually never made, it is even conceivable that two or more people might be exempted for a defect that only one of them actually possesses. Since civilian doctors know their patients only by the names they give, a registrant bent on fraud with a bonafide disqualifying defect which was either intermittent (such as asthma) or unverifiable by objective tests (such as Ménière's syndrome) might receive treatment from several doctors using the names of several conspirators. When the time came for any of the conspirators' physicals, the genuinely unfit registrant would simply obtain a note from the doctor he was seeing under that name. The unqualified registrant's own exemption would remain assured through his regular doctor.

Because the Army rarely bothers to check back with doctors even to verify that they wrote the notes presented at physicals (which, in this case, they would have), it is very likely that this ruse could be perpetrated. However, since it is clearly illegal and, if discovered, would be likely to result in long jail sentences, it seems certain that no registrants would attempt it. That it could be done merely points up the unreliability of the Army's system for determining fitness.

The Army also neglects to protect itself from the foresighted registrant who establishes a history of some disorder unverifiable by laboratory or clinical tests or a record of treatment for a minor disorder whose unpleasantness he has magnified to fit the description of a listed cause for rejection. The individual who has such a history can feel just as assured of being exempted as the person who really has the condition.

Establishing a history of a disorder is often no great problem for those seeking to avoid the draft. Because pain is completely subjective, malingering young men find it easy to enlarge upon minor difficulties. Although doctors can estimate the extent of objective defects, only the patient can say how much it hurts, and sensitivity to pain is known to vary widely among individuals.

Unprepared to deal with those feigning illness, the Army is also deceived by those who are actually unfit but for one reason or the other neglect to claim their exemptions. This category contains some men with homosexual tendencies (2-34*a*[2]) or emotional disturbances (2-33) fearful of public knowledge of their conditions. Bed-wetting, or nocturnal enuresis (2-34*c*), is a defect many young men find embarrassing to admit but which would prove considerably more embarrassing in the Army. Most cases are continuous from childhood and a doctor's record of treatment should be available. However, since this problem is usually psychological in nature and extremely resistant to treatment, medical care may have been foregone in favor of a device which wakes the sleeper when he is voiding. If such a device were used, a psychiatrist's or general practitioner's confirmation of the problem should nevertheless be obtained for use at the physical, but a lengthy medical history would probably not be needed.

Also in this group are young men who do not want to seem to be copping out on what the generals so often call their "military obligation." These youths neglect to call attention to, or obtain verification for, what they consider minor physical defects. Under the Army's faulty system of examination their problems are never discovered. Unfortunately, what was minor in civilian life too often becomes major under the stress of training or combat.

Even the most thorough physical might not uncover a lower back disorder related to habitual bad posture (2-10*d*[3]; see also 2-36). Intermittent pain is often the only symptom of such a defect. If a person with this condition did not seek medical treatment and a letter describing his problem for presentation at his physical, he might put the Army in the unhappy position of drafting him only to discover shortly thereafter that basic training had aggravated his condition and that he would require extensive medical care.

Although the military wants such physical faults brought to their attention, they are unlikely to be interested if a registrant offers no more proof than his complaint at the physical that he has a bad back. According to one lawyer who has handled many draft cases:

> Documentation is especially important as to neck and back conditions. Many civilians have conditions which plague them without being seriously debilitating, just annoying. These are conditions that doctors, lawyers, and insurance companies are used to thinking of as in the whiplash, maybe-it's-there-and-maybe-it-isn't category. Yet such physical conditions can be very serious when a soldier is carrying forty, fifty, or sixty pounds of weight on his back, jumping from great heights, or climbing up things.[1]

Thus every order to report for a preinduction physical includes instructions to the registrant to bring evidence if he has reason to believe that he has a defect that would disqualify him for military service.

Other disorders which have plagued the Army with inductees who are actually unfit include those which no doctor, civilian or military, could uncover if the patient did not describe his symptoms. Among these are Ménière's syndrome (2-6*d*), a progressive disease of the inner ear with intermittent symptoms of dizziness, nausea, ringing in one or both ears, inability to concentrate during an attack, and, usually, advancing deafness.

X-ray findings might confirm that a person suffered from irritable colon (2-3*j*), a recurrent spasm of the large intestine resulting in cramps and frequent bowel movements, but the ailment is characteristically intermittent and might well not be discovered unless the patient complained of it. The condition is usually found in extremely nervous individuals and often lasts over a period of years. Its symptoms are likely to be felt at times of tension, creating general abdominal pain, making it difficult for a person with the problem to withstand the rigors of military service.

Another condition which eludes detection is degenerative joint disease, a type of chronic arthritis (2-11*a*). It is ordinarily a condition of middle life, but sometimes starts in the second decade. Usually hereditary, it often affects one knee and occasionally both. It is a particularly dangerous disease, for both the individual and the Army, because it sneaks up on a person but is likely to be aggravated by exercise or weight bearing. A registrant might ignore this infirmity because the pain at the beginning is characteristically aching, mild, and disappears with rest. X rays and lab tests are usually useless in diagnosis which depends mainly on the patient's description of symptoms and family history.

Degenerative joint disease is only one possible cause of joint pain. A doctor's diagnosis is the only certain way to determine the reason for any discomfort. Although most other kinds of joint disease can be confirmed by objective tests, this is unlikely to happen at an Army preinduction physical. Because joint pain may indicate a condition which might seriously interfere with military duties, young men with this problem should seek medical help before taking their Army examinations.

Theoretically, soldiers should be able to see well enough to avoid running into things and to tell what they're shooting at. However, according to the standards, an inductee can be practically blind in one eye as long as his corrected vision in the other is reasonably acute (2-13). A registrant whose eyesight is slightly on the wrong side of the borderline should probably have his vision checked by an ophthalmologist before reporting for his physical. If it falls into the disqualification category, he should obtain a prescription written for the strength of his new glasses. A registrant without such a prescription, but claiming disqualification, will, according to regulations, have the strength of his glasses checked in addition to having his vision checked with his glasses on. The strength of contact lenses will not be accepted by the Army as proof of disqualifying vision.

Migraine (2-31*b*[2]), a poorly understood illness thought by some authorities to be psychosomatic, is another condition impossible for Army medical examiners or any doctor to verify by tests. A doctor's diagnosis is necessarily based solely on the patient's complaints. Because migraine headaches are undetectable by laboratory and clinical testing, many young men who suffered from them, but did not have doctors' letters attesting that they did, have been erroneously inducted into the Armed Forces. An individual suffering severe and incapacitating migraines would be doing the Army a favor by bringing a physician's report and the medical history of the headaches with him to his physical. Since certain drugs aid in alleviating the pain, he would also be doing himself a favor by seeking medical attention. The person with severe headaches should be completely prepared to describe in detail all his symptoms to his civilian doctor.

A doctor's diagnosis is, of course, the only sure way of determining if a person has any of the conditions mentioned. Although they are undetectable by objective tests, an experienced diagnostician by observation and talking with the patient should be able to determine the problem.

No one should feel foolish in seeking a physician's help if even a suspicion exists that he might be suffering from a condition disqualifying him for the Army. However, to avoid an unnecessary visit, a person would be well advised to investigate the suspected disorder through reference material available in medical school libraries and other sources. Even if this seems to confirm a suspicion of disease, the diagnosis must be left to the doctor. No doctor wants the aid of a lay diagnostician. As one physician put it: "Nothing puts a doctor more uptight than a patient making his diagnosis for him."

By making it the registrant's responsibility to prove his defect, the Army saves the time and expense of performing thorough physicals. But the use of this system makes the potential savings for the registrant even greater—two years of his life, and, if the war continues, perhaps the whole of it.

No problem is too minor to call to the Army's attention, no defect so insignificant that it might not result in exemption.

No one is so healthy that he cannot be an Army medical reject.

4

Psychiatric Unfitness

*"My opinion of this Army and this war
is that nobody in his right mind should be in it."*
—A New York Psychiatrist

IF YOU DON'T WANT TO GO INTO THE ARMY, AND THE
draft puts you uptight, you may be eligible for a
psychiatric exemption. "If you don't want to go,
you're better off and so is the Army if you don't,"
says one psychiatrist who has written more than
fifty letters that resulted in IV-F and I-Y classifications of his patients.

Psychiatrists who see things this way are not rare.
An Ivy League analyst received a phone call while
being interviewed for this book. His end of the con-
versation went like this: "Is there anything pressing

about it—do you have a physical coming up? Do you have reason to believe that your emotional condition is such that it would warrant exemption?" Apparently receiving affirmative answers, he made an appointment with the caller and gave directions to his house. Turning back to the interviewer, he smiled. "That's the second one today," he said.

Another therapist—head of a large suburban mental health center—believes that "anyone who feels strongly enough to ask for an out is not going to be any bargain for the Army, nor is the Army going to do him any good." This doctor maintains that he has only refused one young man who asked for help in establishing mental unfitness for military service. "There was one guy who wanted me to say he was crazy, but he wouldn't take the responsibility of following through and acting crazy!"

This psychiatrist isn't implying that he lies in the letters he writes for his patients. But he does advise them on what hangups might result in exemptions, and then lets them tell the truth about themselves. The truth usually provides sufficient material for a convincing letter.

These therapists, and many others, feel it to be their patriotic and professional duty to warn the Army against potential misfits. It is a service not only to their patients, who might be unable to stand the strain of military life, but also to the Army which loses time, money, and morale while attempting the impossible task of jamming round pegs into square holes.

If you think you might have emotional problems in the Army, it is important to locate a sympathetic psychiatrist to diagnose your difficulties. Whether your problems are severe enough to gain an exemption may depend largely on which psychiatrist you choose. (Information that will help you select a doctor is in Chapter One.)

It is quite possible that psychiatrists may disagree on any man's fitness for the Army. The Department of Defense tries to protect itself from this uncertainty by keeping the criteria for psychiatric rejection extremely ill-defined.

The psychiatric standards are so vague that, unlike other medical standards, they are almost exactly the same for peacetime and for mobilization. As listed in Chapter Two of AR 40-501, the criteria to be used in time of peace or undeclared war (such as Vietnam) are:

SECTION XVI. PSYCHOSES, PSYCHONEUROSES, AND PERSONALITY DISORDERS

2-32. Psychoses   The causes for rejection for appointment, enlistment, and induction are:

Psychosis or authenticated history of a psychotic illness other than those of a brief duration associated with a toxic or infectious process.

2-33. Psychoneuroses   The causes for rejection for appointment, enlistment, and induction are:

a. History of a psychoneurotic reaction which caused—

    (1) Hospitalization.

    (2) Prolonged care by a physician.

    (3) Loss of time from normal pursuits for repeated periods even if of brief duration, or

    (4) Symptoms or behavior of a repeated nature which impaired school or work efficiency.

b. History of a brief psychoneurotic reaction or nervous disturbance within the preceding twelve months which was sufficiently severe to require medical attention or absence from work or school for a brief period (maximum of seven days).

2-34. Personality Disorders The causes for rejection for appointment, enlistment, and induction are:

a. Character and behavior disorders, as evidenced by—

(1) Frequent encounters with law enforcement agencies, or antisocial attitudes or behavior which, while not a cause for administrative rejection, are tangible evidence of an impaired characterological capacity to adapt to the military service.

(2) Overt homosexuality, or other forms of sexual deviant practices such as exhibitionism, transvestism, voyeurism, etc.

(3) Chronic alcoholism or alcohol addiction.

(4) Drug addiction.

b. Character and behavior disorders where it is evident by history and objective examination that the degree of immaturity, instability, personality inadequacy, and dependency will seriously interfere with adjustment in the military service as demonstrated by repeated inability to maintain reasonable adjustment in school, with employers and fellow workers, and other society groups.

c. Other symptomatic immaturity reactions such as authenticated evidence of enuresis which is habitual or persistent, not due to an organic condition (paragraph 2-15*c*), occurring beyond early adolescence (age 12 to 14), and stammering and stuttering of such a degree that the individual is normally unable to express himself clearly or to repeat commands.

d. Specific learning defects secondary to organic or functional mental disorders.

(The wartime standards are precisely the same except that section 2-34*d* is omitted.)

The imprecision of these standards permits the Army much leeway in deciding your acceptability, but it also works to your advantage by leaving open many routes to disqualification. "You could theoretically be rejected for any neurotic trait from bed-wetting to nail-biting," argues one psychiatrist.

Nail-biting, however, would be unlikely to result in an exemption. The two primary concerns the Army will have in deciding whether to induct you will be (1) whether you will create problems for them (for instance, by provoking authority figures to discipline you and spending most of your time in the stockade) and (2) whether your condition will be worsened by military service, making induction clearly unfair for you and burdensome for the Army, which might have to pay a disability pension. To result in an exemption, your problems should be stated in a way that will encourage the Army to have these concerns.

Psychiatrists who have written numerous letters resulting in draft rejections usually describe problems that fall in the following categories:

1. *Conventional psychiatric disorders,* including emotional disturbances suffered at present or in the past such as depression, suicidal or self-destructive thoughts, inability to work, and anxiety. Sleeplessness, and inability to eat due to such disturbances

were also mentioned, as was any psychiatric or psychological counseling ever received by the patient.

2. *Antisocial behavior* as shown by a criminal record, delinquency, history of fights—either verbal or physical—inability to hold a job, drunkenness, lack of closeness to other people, history of rebellion against legitimate authority or other destructive acts or fantasies. If the patient's style of life contrasted with the usual patterns of society or with what would be expected of him in the Army, this information was included.

Some psychiatrists feel that citing difficulties the patient may have had with authority figures is risky: the Army might conclude that authority was not properly administered in the past: "We'll show these wishy-washy psychiatrists that we can put this guy in shape." Thus, if this problem is mentioned, it could be crucial to emphasize that attempts at discipline only met with further resistance. After describing such attempts and their failures, one doctor states that "it is highly unlikely that this client would be amenable to military discipline."[1]

3. *Drug use,* particularly what one therapist calls "chronic and promiscuous" use of hard narcotics, hallucinogens, barbiturates, amphetamines, or other stimulants or depressants, especially when their use forms the core of the patient's life. If a psychotic break ever occurred due to the use of drugs, this was stated.

Information given about drugs should be as specific as the patient will allow. "I think the Army's pretty turned on," says one analyst. "It used to be that you'd say someone was taking drugs and he was out. Now you have to specify what drugs and the extent of use."

4. *Homosexuality,* either overt or latent, or related disturbances such as "problems of sexual identity."

Despite section 2-34*a*(2) of AR 40-501, homosexuality need not be overt in order to be useful in gaining an exemption. "I use the term because the Army understands it," concedes one psychiatrist. "Sex scares the Army. Many patients are unclear about their roles as growing males. With their permission, I can stretch a point and say it would be bad for them to be in an all-male environment, that they have a kind of intriguement with males or are preoccupied with fantasies of a homosexual nature."

Doctors who have composed many successful letters stress that they adhere to the following principles in preparing reports:

* The letter should be recent, written within a month before presentation to the draft board or examining station.
* As much data on overt past history as possible should be included. The duration, extent, nature, and context of problems should be mentioned, as well as any professional care received because of them.
* Specific information and examples rather than broad general statements should be emphasized. For instance, if drugs are involved, kinds and amounts should be described. If a patient's way of living is considered incompatible with making it in the Army, it should be detailed, rather than simply called, for example, a "marginal existence."
* The letter is written for review by laymen and should avoid professional gobbledygook.
* The "shotgun approach" is useful. As many problems as possible ought to be mentioned.

* The psychiatrist should state, usually as a closing, that he considers the patient unsuitable for the Army. One doctor's favorite phrase for getting this across is: "As a psychiatrist, I feel that you should have some concern about inducting (————). I strongly recommend that he be examined by a military psychiatrist."

Many psychiatrists believe the *implications* the letter makes concerning a young man's potential troubles and possible lack of performance in the Army are especially important. "The more you kind of hint at a thing, the greater the chance of exemption," suggests one therapist.

It is extremely useful for the psychiatrist to suggest that the patient's condition may worsen in the Army. An example would be the individual who "needs isolation in order to maintain his sense of self." A word of caution might also be inserted about the patient's continued need for therapy. But any advice to the military should be carefully worded so that it does not sound like a threat or an order. "The Army is much more likely to be frightened than threatened," says a knowledgeable psychiatrist. However, Army regulations state that "the mere possibility that a psychiatric condition will arise later in the military service should not be sufficient reason in itself for disqualification; however, such a possibility should be considered in light of other findings."[2]

The wording of the psychiatrist's report may be more important than its factual content. Thus young men whose only hangup was the draft have been rejected by the Army.

One psychiatrist who has aided many draft-age patients—"anyone who walks through my door seeking help is a patient"—maintains that the prospect of induction very commonly causes young men to suffer great anxiety and the feeling that their lives are being controlled by forces which they cannot direct. Their anxiety may cause them to lose sleep and eat poorly. Daydreams of self-destructive acts which would disqualify them for the Army (such as chopping off fingers or toes) are common, as are plans to go on long drug- or alcohol-induced trips. Some even think of suicide, while others plot elaborate and ill-conceived schemes for destroying the government or blowing up the White House. "As a public-spirited citizen," smiled the doctor, "I would object to the Army taking these guys. If I were a general, I'd worry about them giving aid and comfort to the enemy."

Once you have chosen your psychiatrist, you should feel perfectly free to level with him about your problems. The more information he has, the more help he can be. However, even your reluctance to talk to him may give him grounds for advising the Army against your induction. Dr. Neal Blumenfeld, a Berkeley, California, psychiatrist, has written:

> Even though consciously the patient wants you to find something that will help him get out of the draft, unconsciously he regards you as any other patient would, that is, he's afraid you will think there's something seriously wrong with him or that he's crazy, so that he will often withhold information from you. This is potentially a serious problem in reports, but it is also a potential asset. If you find a patient who is particularly guarded and suspicious, this can be a piece of data that can be quite valuable in your report. Is he so guarded and

suspicious that he is actually acting in a self-destructive manner in that he is not cooperating with you?[3]

Once you have asked for a letter to take with you to your physical, most psychiatrists will automatically confer with you about what you want it to say. Obviously, this is a perfect opportunity for you to advise him, if he happens to be inexperienced at writing draft letters, on exactly what it should say. Again, most psychiatrists will show you the letter and ask your reactions to it. If he doesn't want you to see it, better look for another psychiatrist.

If you happen to be seeing a clinical psychologist, a letter from him in addition to one from a psychiatrist may help you get an exemption, but you will not be exempted on the basis of a letter from a psychologist alone. The Army gives no weight to the testimony of psychologists, who do not have medical degrees, unless it is supported by the opinion of psychiatrists, who do.

The letter should be presented at your physical. All evidence indicates that your chances of getting an exemption are better there than at a medical interview with your draft board, particularly in borderline cases. Because of the vagaries of the psychiatric standards, almost all psychiatric cases should be considered borderline. (See also Chapters One and Six.)

Because of the haphazard and understaffed nature of most physicals, you might not be examined by a psychiatrist even though you are seeking a psychiatric exemption and even if your letter recommends it. Army regulations state that

a specific psychiatric evaluation will be made by the Chief, Medical Examining Section, whenever the examining physician has reason to question the examinee's emotional, social, or intellectual adequacy for military service. Such examinees may be referred to a psychiatrist when the services of such a specialist can be made available within a period of two days. When the services of a psychiatrist cannot be made available within two days, or when such referral is not deemed necessary, the medical officer will make the final psychiatric evaluation.[4]

If you do get to see a military psychiatrist, probably he will not attempt to knock down your letter and in most cases will only ask one or two perfunctory questions.

Folk tales concerning military physicals abound. One is that if a guy wants a psychiatric exemption, he should really put on a show for the Army—not bathe for two or three weeks, dress in his weirdest clothes, and drop an acid cube before appearing. The difficulty with this theory is that it probably won't work. If a person is high, the Army can hold him until he comes down. The duds and dirt most likely won't bother them at all. They may just lick their lips over the prospect of inducting him and "straightening him out." On the other hand, if your natural style is East Village, there's no need to go to your physical looking like Wall Street.

If you have a letter from a psychiatrist—and you must if you want an exemption—no acting out is necessary and may even be harmful. "My experience," says one doctor, "is that if a person comes in and says 'I have this wrong with me and basically I don't want to go,' they get uptight. If you get an officer uptight, he gets punitive." Punitive at your physical means declaring you fit for induction.

Many people who feel they would qualify for a psychiatric exemption are reluctant to attempt to get one. They don't want the information that they were rejected for psychiatric reasons to be in their draft files, accessible not only to the Army and Selective Service System, but in practice to any government agency. This is certainly a legitimate concern, particularly for anyone who might someday seek public office or a high position in government.

Some protection may be gained by asking your psychiatrist to request in his letter that it be returned to him because of its confidential nature once it has been evaluated only by proper medical authorities. There is probably a good chance that your draft board will comply when your folder is returned to them. If they don't, ask your doctor to write directly to the board requesting its return. Lawyers who have handled draft cases where psychiatric unfitness was argued have been successful in getting psychiatrists' reports returned on the grounds that they are confidential, meant to be seen only by doctors, and (if the letter was sealed when presented at the physical) might cause the patient a "psychic shock" if he ever saw it in his draft folder.

It sometimes happens that letters are handed back to disqualified examinees at their physicals. This cannot be counted on, however. According to Army regulations, your doctor's report is supposed to be attached to official medical records; obviously, some medical examiners either don't know this or don't care. If you are told that you have been disqualified, you might politely ask if you could have the letter back.

Even if you do succeed in getting your doctor's

letter returned, the psychiatric nature of your disqualification, along with a brief notation from the medical examiner giving the reason it was granted, will remain in your file.

Some young men who couldn't care less whether they have a psychiatric rejection in their files—as long as they have a rejection—hesitate to seek a psychiatric exemption for another reason. Psychiatric treatment is notoriously expensive, and they feel that they can't afford this way out. However, time and diligence in seeking the *right* psychiatrist can reduce the expense factor. The right psychiatrist can often diagnose a draft problem and prescribe civilian status in one or two visits. The grapevine around so-called hippie establishments as well as the information in Chapter One should speed the process of locating a sympathetic doctor. Every doctor, however, will appreciate some tact when you approach him with your problem.

You may also worry that if the psychiatrist's report mentions drugs, the "narcs" will soon be on your trail. None of the psychiatrists interviewed, including one who cited drug use in dozens of letters, reported any problems suffered by their patients in this area. They advised, however, that wisdom suggests not bringing drugs to the examining station.

It is highly unlikely that any checking will be done on anything stated in your letter. In the great majority of cases, the Army does not even check with your doctor to make sure he wrote the letter. Occasionally, they ask for further information or records, but this is rare and can be met by your psychiatrist writing back to say he won't release anything without your permission. In every case heard of when researching this book, that action ended the correspondence and did not affect the exemption.

The fear of having a psychiatric exemption somehow haunting them throughout their lives makes many men forego this possible alternative to military service. The Army is happy to foster this fear, although it may be based more on fantasy than fact.

Consider the case of Pvt. Novotny, the central figure in Philip Roth's short story, "Novotny's Pain." Drafted during the Korean War, Novotny suddenly began to suffer a horrible back pain. The Army doctors, unable to find any objective cause for his discomfort, sent him to a military psychiatrist who, in turn, reported his findings to the colonel in charge of orthopedics.

The colonel told Novotny that the psychiatrist had determined that he was a "passive-aggressive." What this meant, the colonel said, was that he was yellow. He could, if he wanted, get a psychiatric discharge, but it would follow him the rest of his life. Everyone would know that he was chicken.

Novotny, who really did have an unbearable back pain, reluctantly took the discharge. He went home and got married. He found a good job. And no one ever asked him why he had been discharged.

5

Moral Unfitness

A MAN WHO MURDERED AS A CIVILIAN IS UNACCEPT-
able to the Army, which trains men to kill. A convicted arsonist cannot be inducted for shipment to
Vietnam, where American soldiers burn villages. In
short, citizens whose demonstrated talents indicate
the greatest potential are summarily rejected by the
military.

Only those who meet certain "moral standards"
can be drafted. Ideally, these standards would im-
pose an upper limit, and none too principled would
be inducted. But, while a conscientious objector
might well feel he is morally unfit to be a soldier,
the Army's criteria paradoxically preclude only the
least moral.

Simply stated, the moral standards provide draft

exemptions for youths with a criminal record or a subversive background. But the criteria are vague and their application uneven. Few men are actually found morally unfit—only one or two of every hundred who pass through the examination mill. And when draft calls are high, the Army manages to find more criminals rehabilitated and discovers fewer Communists even among those who claim a subversive past.

There are three significant forms you will be given to fill out at the beginning of the preinduction physical: a Report of Medical History (SF 89, see Chapter Six), the Armed Forces Security Questionnaire (DD 98), and a mimeographed sheet for listing criminal violations. The latter two are used to determine your moral suitability for military service.

Moral or political rejects are termed "administratively disqualified" and classified either IV-F or I-Y. The determination is subjective, and those found unacceptable are often simply youths deemed not likely to turn out well as soldiers. "The I-Y classification is a sort of dumping ground," explained a New York lawyer active in draft cases. "It's a place for guys the Army just doesn't want and it's often very hard to find out why they were put there."

A youth may be found administratively unfit by either his local draft board, if the proper information has been presented to it, or by the Army as a result of the physical and subsequent investigation. As in the medical area, most moral-political disqualifications are made by the Army.

The uncertainty of being rejected for either criminal or subversive conduct must be stressed. A psychiatric or medical problem is more likely to gain an exemption. But thousands are administratively disqualified, and membership in a suspect organization or a court record could help a borderline medical case.

"Kid," the man at the examining station growled, "we only got one question: have you ever been arrested?" Well, Arlo Guthrie explained about how he had been busted for dumping some trash by a roadside, and then he revealed in five-part harmony at the Newport Folk Festival that he had been rejected by the Army as a dangerous litterbug, and next they made a movie spreading the tale in technicolor.

A year ago, the men at the Pentagon compiled a list of crimes, including some you could commit and still be moral enough to serve. And they must have got to thinking about the Alice's Restaurant Anti-Massacree Movement and other types not anxious to fulfill their military obligation. Because they weren't taking any chances.

Right there, in AR 601-270, section W-2, appendix W—among the offenses *not* cause for rejection —the eleventh item on the list, between "drunk in public" and "fornication," is "dumping refuse near highway."

Cattle rustling, on the other hand, might get you an exemption. It is listed among the felonies.

Generally, it will take a felony conviction or a long string of lesser offenses to escape the draft, but misdemeanor adjudications arising from civil rights or antiwar demonstrations sometimes result in I-Y classification. The latter, however, will depend largely on local prejudice and could mean speedy induction by a "law and order" board.

Moreover, no criminal record guarantees exemption.[1] It only ensures that you will be screened by military authorities who will decide if you are welcome despite a checkered past. Unlike a waiver of medical unfitness, which must be requested by the registrant, a "moral waiver" is considered routinely and does not need your approval.

Army regulations require the same screening process for youths having "frequent difficulties with law enforcement agencies, criminal tendencies, a history of antisocial behavior, alcoholism, drug addiction, sexual misconduct, questionable moral character, or traits of character which make [them] unfit to associate with other men."

Simply indicating these problems on the form provided at your physical is, however, quite unlikely to get you disqualified. On the other hand, the same problems described by a private psychiatrist will probably result in your being found medically unfit (see Chapter Four).

It may take the Army months to judge your moral suitability, or your morality may be certified acceptable before you have left the examining station. Conviction of a single minor offense—such as vagrancy, vandalism, disturbance of the peace, or dumping refuse near a highway—is automatically overlooked. Most traffic violations, regardless of number, are likewise ignored. And the examining station commander can forgive on the spot a record of up to three four-month sentences.

Other crimes are divided into two categories: those carrying a maximum penalty of one year in jail (misdemeanors) and those punishable by more than a year's imprisonment (felonies). A registrant whose record places him in either of the categories is supposed to undergo a "moral waiver investigation" before becoming eligible for induction. In fact, the investigation is often skipped or cut short, and standards appear to fall when draft calls rise.

Conviction of a misdemeanor is not, by itself, disqualifying. Regulations specifically state that "induction will not be denied solely on [that] basis," and provide for a quick waiver by the local Army Recruiting District Commander. Frequent brushes with the law and other episodes which might indicate "questionable moral character" can be officially excused at the same level.

Anyone found guilty of a felony, no matter what the actual sentence imposed or the time served, is morally unfit—unless given the stamp of approval by the Armed Forces Moral Waiver Determination Board. A complete record of schooling and employment is taken and, if necessary, an investigation into police and court records is made.

Those who have committed "serious offenses" or are judged to have "ingrained delinquency behavior patterns" are classified IV-F or I-Y (i.e., too immoral to kill or be killed). The remaining registrants are considered under the Army's strikingly advanced concept that "an individual is composed of his mental-moral-medical abilities and functions as a whole being." The formula is explained in regulations as follows:

> . . . a court record combined with marginal medical and mental abilities predicts marginal functioning. Registrants with the aforementioned mental-moral-medical pattern have difficulty adjusting to military stress and job performance demands. In

addition to making a marginal contribution in the service they often become disciplinary problems.[2]

In simple language, you need not have a really bad criminal record, fail the mental test, or be medically unfit to avoid military service. Being a borderline case in two or three of the areas may do the trick.

In addition, all men charged with violating a state or federal law—except minor traffic statutes and the Selective Service Act—who have not yet had their day in court are draft exempt as long as the charge is still pending. Classified I-Y, they are liable to induction if cleared of the alleged crime, or, if found guilty, after serving their sentence. Draft free are all those under parole, probation, suspended sentence, or conditional release from imprisonment. But they can be inducted on a waiver if their local boards "obtain a complete release from all forms of civil restraint."

If unhappy with the moral waiver procedure followed in your case, you can appeal, but the lack of specific standards will make a successful challenge difficult. Registered letters may be sent to your local Army Recruiting District Commander or to either of the following:

Commanding General
U. S. Army Recruiting Command
Attn: Armed Forces Moral Waiver
Determination Board
Hampton, Virginia 23369

Executive Agent for AFEES
Deputy Chief of Staff for Personnel
Attn: PD, Department of the Army
Washington, D.C. 20310

"Among the thousands of men and women coming into the Armed Forces each month, we must recognize that there might be a certain number of subversives and spies working for the Communist enemy," warned the official statement supposed to be read to all prospective draftees at their preinduction physical. "This," it continued, "is part of the 'boring' from within tactics of the Communist conspiracy."

Although this McCarthy era diatribe was toned down a year ago, the Pentagon still relies on the same clever counterscheme to foil the diabolical forces which would infiltrate the military: it asks the subversives to identify themselves.

To screen out those whose induction "is not clearly consistent with the interests of national security," all registrants are "given the opportunity" to fill out the Armed Forces Security Questionnaire (DD 98). The form names some 275 groups and movements on the Attorney General's red list and asks you to disclose any past or present connection with the tainted organizations.

Unfortunately, despite the Army's rhetoric, its real dread of infiltration seems to be slight. It is difficult to gain an exemption as a political reject. Merely admitting membership in a subversive group will not necessarily keep you out of the service.

The questionnaire will be handed to you at the beginning of the physical with the implication that this form, like all others, is routine and should be filled out quickly. An officer will suggest that you simply answer all questions of participation in subversive activities negatively; indeed, there might be a wall chart with the answers already filled in, to demonstrate the "proper" method of completing the questionnaire.

You are, of course, not to be alarmed that the Government is inquiring into your political beliefs and associations. Most likely you will be spared listening to the orientation lecture in the assembly line rush, but some of it is worth quoting, as a guide to the military mind:

> The fact that you are signing a security questionnaire at this time does not call into question your loyalty to the United States or your intention to serve in the Armed Forces with the honor and fidelity traditional to the American soldier. The questionnaire is simply a means of helping the Federal Government protect itself and you against subversion in the Armed Forces.
>
> As a member of the Armed Forces you will occupy a position of honor and trust. It is vital to our national security that all such positions of honor and trust be held by persons of complete and unswerving loyalty to the United States.[3]

If you have no intention of serving in the Armed Forces—with or without the honor and fidelity traditional to the American soldier—there are several points to remember in approaching the security questionnaire.

First, whatever might be said to the contrary at your physical, completion of the form is *not* mandatory. Conscientious objectors are specifically exempted from filling out the questionnaire, and all others may refuse to do so without violating any law, including the Selective Service code. You cannot be penalized for your refusal.

Indeed, your rights are clearly stated on the form itself: ". . . in accordance with the Fifth Amendment of the Constitution of the United States you cannot be compelled to furnish any statements which you may reasonably believe may lead to your prosecution for a crime." Although you may have other reasons for your refusal, the self-incrimination provision of the Fifth Amendment is the only sure protection against possible reprisal.[4] There is absolutely no need to explain why you feel the Fifth Amendment is applicable in your case.

Declining to fill out DD 98, however, will not win you an exemption. In the past such action sometimes triggered an induction-delaying investigation, but under new regulations the Army will not stop long enough to find out what you are hiding before putting you in uniform. Non-co-operation will now serve only as a gesture of indignation against governmental invasion of private beliefs.

If you are more interested in remaining a civilian than in protesting official snooping, confess subversive affiliations. There are several ways in which to do this, and in deciding your proper course it is important to remember that connection with a suspect organization does not ensure rejection.

Study the list of organizations on the form (reprinted in the Appendix). These are groups "reported by the Attorney General as having significance in connection with National Security." There are about 275 of them with frightening sounding names like American Women for Peace, Chopin Cultural Center, and Maryland Congress Against Discrimination. ("Misleading titles," the Army explains, "intended to cloak their true mission and attract the unwary.")

You are not limited to the Attorney General's

selection (which does appear passé), and indeed the form specifically inquires:

> Are you now or have you ever been a member of any organization, association, movement, group, or combination of persons not on the Attorney General's list which advocates the overthrow of our constitutional form of government, or which has adopted the policy of advocating or approving the commission of acts of force or violence to deny other persons their rights under the Constitution of the United States, or which seeks to alter the form of government of the United States by unconstitutional means?

But admission of such nefarious activities, once a possible cause for rejection, will now not even get you investigated. Until recently, the slightest deviation on the security questionnaire—failure to answer one item, hedging on a single response—required a full-scale probe prior to induction. But regulations now make it clear that "one who refuses to complete DD Form 98 or who qualifies the form by refusing to acknowledge whether or not he is a member of an organization on the Attorney General's list or a Communist will be eligible for induction . . ."

"There are a great number of organizations which do nothing but counsel people how to avoid the draft," confided a top intelligence official explaining the change in policy. "So we had numerous cases where these guys wouldn't answer questions or gave some group or another that wasn't on the list, and all they were doing was wasting a lot of time.

"Now we've decided," he continued, "it's better to take the risk than to spend the time investigating these types."

Only by labeling yourself a Communist or admitting membership in a group officially certified subversive can you delay and possibly escape being drafted. A registrant who confesses either status "will not be inducted into the Armed Forces pending completion of a thorough investigation."[5]

While the Army Intelligence Command is making that inquiry, you are deferred and should receive a form (DD 62) with the following notation: "Acceptability for induction held in abeyance; not presently acceptable for induction."

The investigation, to be carried out in accordance with AR 604-10, begins at the examining station. The officer in charge will hand you a second form, Statement of Personal History (DD 398, see Appendix). In addition to a series of questions on security similar to those asked in DD 98, the new form delves into educational and family background, travel to foreign lands, relatives living abroad, previous employment and residences, etc. The same Fifth Amendment rights apply, and you need not provide any information which might be incriminating.

In addition, an officer will interview you, ask why you refused to complete the forms or inquire into the nature of admitted activities. He is likely to suggest that you are making a mistake, that perhaps you did not understand, that the consequences could be far-reaching, that this could affect your status in the Army. You need not answer his questions, volunteer a statement, or remain at the station to "reconsider."

Unfortunately, despite its own regulations, the required "thorough investigation" often goes no further. The "induction held in abeyance" form never arrives, and the registrant is treated like all others found medically and mentally acceptable.

Because the Army neglects to investigate possible security risks, a youth who intends to admit subversive activity would be well-advised to consult a lawyer familiar with this field even before reporting for his physical. (There are few attorneys really qualified to provide assistance; check with local draft resistance unions or the area chapter of the National Lawyers Guild to locate a lawyer with the necessary experience.)

Some attorneys report that they have obtained desired results by insisting upon an investigation to protect their admittedly radical clients from less-than-honorable discharge after induction.

In cases where the investigation has not been made despite disclosure of a subversive background, or where a youth was never given the DD 98 questionnaire, his lawyer should write to:

Army Intelligence Command
Fort Holabird
Baltimore, Md. 21219

and/or

Assistant Chief of Staff for Intelligence
Department of the Army
Washington, D.C. 20310

Attorneys who have successfully handled such cases take the following approach in their letters: My client wants the Army to know about his political background; while the Army may wish to waive its required investigation, that investigation also guarantees his protection after induction. He is willing to waive the protection ensured by the inquiry if the Army will guarantee that he will not be discharged as a result of the beliefs and activities he has disclosed or wishes to disclose.

This formula has, at least in several cases, produced an induction-delaying investigation and has even resulted in exemption without significant inquiry. However, a New York draft lawyer warns: "This is not the sort of thing which can be used by someone who has nothing to say, no political background."

(A Ninth Circuit Federal Appeals Court decision recently held that failure to allow a registrant the opportunity to fill out a security questionnaire was justifiable cause for him to refuse induction, because information supplied on the form might have disqualified him from military service.)

When the Army does choose to investigate, the probe will attempt to determine the extent of the registrant's involvement in the subversive organization's activities. It is impossible to report with accuracy how long such an inquiry generally takes or what per cent of those investigated are rejected, because Army intelligence has classified this information "for official use only." However, those familiar with this area say that the probe, which often used to last nine months to a year, now seldom takes longer than three months.

Some observers suggest that it is best to admit subversive affiliations but refuse to give details, because in such cases the investigation is more time-consuming. DD 98 asks a full explanation of affiliations confessed, but the fact that you have conceded membership in a listed group does not obligate you to name that group. Here again, you are fully protected by the Fifth Amendment.

The degree of participation, and not the fact of membership, is the controlling factor in deciding who is safe to induct.[6] When draft calls are high, more chances are taken. Among the circumstances officials are advised to consider are length of membership, your age at the time, your awareness of the subversive nature of the group, the role you played in its activities, and the reasons advanced for joining. As an example of an acceptable reason, the regulations cite: "to obtain low-cost insurance." Try using that when the Government wants to keep you out of something rather than get you in ("Yes, I joined the Revolutionary Assassination League to take advantage of their charter-flight deal").

Some registrants with a subversive background use a degree of creativity in seeking to avoid military service, while others feel it is their responsibility to be inducted and thus in a position to disrupt the Army.

Youths sometimes write anonymous letters about themselves to their draft boards or have friends flood the board with mail. The letters express grave suspicions about the registrant's loyalty, serious doubts about his patriotism, and even unsettling hints of treason. "I had one client who tried this," a San Francisco attorney reported, "but we never found out what effect it all had because he got out with a psychiatric thing." It probably won't have any effect. Regulations used to require a security investigation when accusations were received "from any source," but the new policy is to consider only "credible derogatory information" from *reliable* sources. Of course, if you have reliable friends . . .

Then there's the case of SDS leader Mark Rudd,

who asked his draft board for an occupational deferment as a professional revolutionary. Apparently not agreeing that plying his trade was essential to the national health, safety, or interest, his board refused to grant the request. Rudd promptly informed them that he was ready to be inducted, but warned that he fully intended to continue to follow his calling once in the Army. At last report, he was found "physically unfit" by a team of medical examiners under somewhat mysterious circumstances. The Army is apparently uneasy about drafting youths who announce their intention to disrupt.

Army regulations call for all those found politically unfit to be classified IV-F.[7] In reality, most individuals who are determined security risks are assigned a I-Y. If found acceptable, you may challenge the ruling by writing to:

Assistant Chief of Staff for Intelligence
Department of the Army
Washington, D.C. 20310

If rejected as too radical, Army Headquarters will send a copy of your file to the FBI, which, if you deserved the exemption, probably knew about you in the first place.

There is only one risk in seeking to escape the draft as a subversive: the Government will never hire you for any position requiring a security clearance. On the other hand, as the orientation lecture notes: "When you fill out your questionnaire as all loyal Americans are expected to, you contribute to your own welfare and that of the United States, *into whose service you will soon enter*."

6

The Preinduction Physical

THE ARMED FORCES EXAMINING AND ENTRANCE
Stations can perhaps best be compared to the stock-
yards, where the cattle are herded in and inspected,
the diseased animals rejected, and the healthy sent
to slaughter.

"We deliver to market, the rest is up to the
buyer," said a spokesman for Selective Service headquarters asked to explain his agency's role in the
preinduction physical.

The "buyer" is the Army and the physical is its
private affair. It sets the standards, makes the examination, and determines acceptability. And it demon-
strates that it can be as arbitrary and inequitable as
any draft board.

Two of every five draftees undergoing physical

examinations since 1950 have been rejected as unfit
for military service. Half were medically disqualified,
most of the others failed to meet intelligence standards, and a small number were found morally unacceptable.

All these men should have been judged by the
same yardstick, for the law requires that an official
list of fitness criteria be prescribed. But, in practice,
the standards of acceptability vary according to the
need for men, and, at the same time, differ from
state to state.

Over five and a half million draft registrants are
now classified IV-F or I-Y, while about six and a
half million are in uniform or have completed their
military service. Chance—not health or intelligence
—separates many in the two groups. A soldier from
Michigan might well still be a civilian had he lived in
Massachusetts, and a young man found acceptable
in February may have been rejected had he been
examined in July.

In the early sixties, some observers noted with
alarm that more than half the nation's youths were
flunking their physicals. But declining fitness was not
the cause of the rising rejection rate. It was simply
that in the interim between Korea and Vietnam fewer
men were needed. Manipulation of the standards
sent the rejection rate, about one-third during the
Korean War, soaring to over fifty per cent while
peace prevailed, and then plummeting back to just
slightly more than a third when American troops
started pouring into Vietnam in late 1965.

In 1967 a national average of 40.7 per cent of
those examined for military service were found unfit. But a youth from Oklahoma (22.8 per cent) or

North Dakota (24.0 per cent) had less than half the chance of being exempted as one from Alabama (50.8 per cent) or Mississippi (50.6 per cent). The low education and income levels of the deep South partially explain this great disparity. But what accounts for the sixteen-point spread between Michigan (31.2 per cent) and Massachusetts (47.5 per cent)? Both states have high per capita incomes and a similar sociological make-up. Uneven application of the standards must be the answer.

The Army publishes an approved list of medical standards "to insure uniformity in the medical evaluation of candidates for military service." What then, if not local prejudice, explains the fact that examiners in Oklahoma reject only 16 per cent as medically disqualified while those in Arizona declare more than 39 per cent medically unfit? And are the youths of North Dakota (18.9 per cent) really that much healthier than those of Idaho (38.7 per cent)?

Moreover, unless Negroes are hardier as a race than whites, there must be something deficient about the physical examinations which, in 1967, found almost a third of the whites but just a sixth of the blacks medically unacceptable.[1]

The explanation is not complex. The physical is a haphazard mass processing in which unclaimed defects are likely to go unnoticed. Young men coming from middle- or upper-class backgrounds, who have had regular medical attention all their lives, are certain to be better supplied with evidence of disqualifying conditions than their low income counterparts.

"The attitudes of preinductees toward military life," reads the Army's physical examination manual, "will be influenced by the manner in which they are treated during preinduction processing." The Resistance could not ask more. For even the youth who does not arrive at his physical feeling threatened and resentful is likely to leave disturbed by the military's lack of concern for the individual and nonplused by its bureaucratic inefficiency.

"Registrants will be treated with courtesy and maximum attention will be given to the preinductee's welfare," the manual continues. But the "preinductee's welfare" often seems the Army's last concern. Take the case of one youth at a Baltimore physical who fainted after his blood test. As the young man fell to the floor, the physician who had been taking blood samples rushed to his aid. He was immediately ordered back to work by an Army doctor, who looked down at the suddenly pale youth and demanded, "You can get up, can't you?" When no answer came, the doctor hoisted him up on a wooden bench. He lay there for two hours without further medical attention.

The manual instructs that "all phases of preinduction processing will be conducted in a dignified and professional manner." There is nothing dignified or professional, however, about the assembly-line inspections. A doctor who goes up on one side of a line checking twenty-five right ears and down the other side checking twenty-five left ears is hardly following the highest standards of his calling. An orthopedic evaluation, which regulations suggest be done individually and never in groups of more than six, is often conducted for one hundred at a time.

It is not surprising, then, that thousands of men are discharged from the Army each year with disqualifying conditions overlooked at their physicals.

A Selective Service spokesman excused this situation with the observation, "There are a lot of disabilities people have which don't show up until the guy is running through the Army grinder."

For a better explanation one need not look further than former draft director General Hershey. In a 1966 interview with *U.S. News and World Report,* Hershey was asked if the physicals were efficiently administered. His candid answer follows:

> They're doing their best. The trouble is, how do you go from handling 4,000 men a month to 40,000—just like that? Of course, their people said, "Go out and hire more doctors." All right, they hire doctors. Whom do they get?
>
> Two kinds: One is the doctor from the service, who is the boy who was an intern last year, and he's doing his two years of compulsory duty in uniform. So he goes down to the induction station and he's in charge; a kid who's learned a little about disease but doesn't know much about what a well man looks like. But he's supposed to be picking out the "wells," not the sick.
>
> Then he has to hire somebody to help him. Usually all you can get is part-time doctors. Generally, that means the ones who have a little spare time and these are the ones who haven't got many patients.
>
> You also need clerks. "Well," you say, "why worry about clerks?"
>
> I'm worrying a great deal, because when a doctor goes down a line of naked men saying what's wrong with each of them and a clerk is coming along behind him copying down what the doctor says, and when he gets through that, the clerk doesn't know what he's written, or doesn't under-

stand all the terms—then the poor doctor sits down and says, "I wonder what I could have said there about that man."[2]

The shamefully inadequate physical leaves little chance for the registrant who knows of no disqualifying defect, but hopes "they will find something wrong with me." On the other hand, its hurried inefficiency can be a boon to those who arrive prepared.

The preinduction physical begins in the half-lit predawn hours in front of your local board. Tired, dispirited youths, most recognizing the full reality of the draft threat for the first time, mill about waiting for the chartered buses to ship them en masse to the examining station.

Selective Service regulations require the registrant not only to report for his physical, but to complete it, and to "obey the orders of the representatives of the Armed Forces [and to] submit to such examination as the commanding officer of the examining station shall direct."[3]

If you refuse to take all, or any part of the physical, you will risk prosecution for violating the draft law and face a possible five-year jail term and a $10,000 fine. Somewhat anticlimactically, Army regulations further threaten that non-co-operators will not be allowed to board homebound buses. (Conscientious objectors failing to take their physicals will be treated as if they had been found acceptable.)[4]

Unless you decide that complete non-co-operation with the war machine is your only course, it is best to confront the military-draft bureaucracy by following its rules while exploiting its weaknesses. There is some chance that a disruptive registrant—one who distributes antiwar leaflets at the examining station or refuses to keep on his undershorts when told to undress—will be administratively rejected. But there is a great risk that officials will instead seek to ensure his induction. If you have a defect to claim and a doctor's letter to substantiate it, look at the physical as an opportunity and do nothing to jeopardize your exemption.

Your draft board will forward to the physical only information presented to it concerning your fitness and one form (Record of Induction, DD 47). That form does not contain even the brief physical description supplied when you registered at eighteen, and the Army examiners will have no other information or make any further attempt to identify you. Thus it is quite possible that an unfit friend with a letter bearing your name could take your physical. Medical rejects are rarely investigated and the ploy would likely succeed; but such action is clearly illegal and certainly not advisable given the numerous legal routes to disqualification.

The physical itself is divided into three parts: the completion of required forms; the mental test; and the medical examination.

There are three significant forms you will be given to fill out: a medical history report (SF 89, see Appendix), the Armed Forces Security Questionnaire (DD 98, see Appendix), and a record of criminal violations. The latter two, used to determine your moral acceptability for military service, are discussed at length in Chapter Five.

In completing your medical history report, be sure

your answers conform to the information in your doctor's letter. The form, used by all government agencies, lists a series of diseases, defects, and conditions and provides a space to note unlisted problems. Don't neglect to mention any of your troubles. A description of difficulties in school work and employment is specifically requested; it is a good place to note the problems caused by your disqualifying condition. One other item is important: it asks for a "statement of examinee's present health." If you are unfit for military service (or hope to be), the answer is "poor." Regulations require that the Army examiner discuss all indicated medical problems "to assist in evaluating the examinee's background and to protect the individual and the Government in the event of future claims for disability or aggravation of disability."[5] In reality, the examiner is likely to show little interest in any condition not substantiated by a doctor's letter.

Even if you do not have a letter, however, go ahead and claim your disability. Regulations further require that, if your complaint is neither backed by corroborating evidence nor confirmed by examination, the following entry be made in official records:

> Registrant is determined acceptable; however, he claims ailments unverified by the medical officers and has been advised to present documentary evidence at his own expense to substantiate claims to his Selective Service local board prior to his induction.[6]

This notation should be made in item 73 of the Report of Medical Examination (SF 88); if the doctor fails to do so, call it to his attention. Proof that you claimed unfitness at your physical could strengthen your appeal, for which the procedure is set out in Chapter Seven.

Because the military needs men bright enough to follow orders, draftees are tested to determine their mental ability. When the form-filling session is over, the Armed Forces Qualification Test is administered. Anyone smart enough to flunk is rejected. Unfortunately, the Army's intelligence standards are low, the test is designed to expose fakers, and those who have had at least a tenth grade education will be hard pressed to fail convincingly.

"Emphasis will be placed on the fact," the proctor's manual instructs, "that a deliberate attempt to fail the mental tests will not keep [registrants] out of the military service since they will be inducted, regardless of their scores, if they are found not trying to do their best."

The passing score on the AFQT is thirty-one, except for high school graduates who need only ten. All others scoring between ten and thirty are retested, declared acceptable if they pass a series of aptitude tests, and given a I-Y if they do not. Those who get less than ten are classified IV-F.[7]

However, an Army psychologist reviews the records of registrants not considered "true failures," and of all who score between ten and thirty regardless of the outcome of retesting. Youths found to have never advanced beyond the ninth grade are disqualified. But all others are interviewed by a psychologist, and those determined "poorly motivated [but] capable of passing" are administratively accepted. In doubtful cases, a psychiatric consultation and an investigation of schooling and employment are authorized.[8]

The complex and arbitrary system by which the mentally fit are separated from the mentally unfit produces some strange inequities. The high school graduate who scores only ten is, by decree, intelligent enough to be a soldier, while the high school dropout who scores thirty is judged too weak-minded to serve. But the same high school graduate who can be drafted against his will with a score of between ten and thirty would be turned down if he tried to enlist (thirty-one required).

Manipulation of the fitness standards to keep the rejection rate in line with the draft calls is most blatant in the setting of mental criteria. When the calls are low, the intelligence requirements are high; when cannon fodder is needed to fill the trenches (or rice paddies), the requirements drop accordingly. Thus, in November 1965, as American troops began to saturate Vietnam, the standards, raised only two years earlier, were lowered. They fell again in April 1966, further in October of that year, and hit the present level in December 1966. The result: mental disqualifications, which had been running at more than a fifth, plunged below 11 per cent in 1966 and to almost 9 per cent in 1967.[9]

In a June 1966 hearing, House Armed Services Committee Chairman Rep. L. Mendel Rivers suggested that too many were escaping the draft as physical rejects. We ought to get back, Rivers declared, to World War II standards, when "they didn't examine your eyes and arms, they counted them." Thousands of young men who have experienced the preinduction medical examination could easily believe Rivers's proposal had been adopted. Some would go so far as to suggest its adoption would be an improvement.

The examination is the final step in preinduction processing and lasts several hours, depending on the number of bodies to be inspected. Most of your time will be spent waiting in lines.

Most of the clinical evaluation, such as it is, will be accomplished en masse, with registrants standing in rows an arm's length apart while several doctors check various organs with a rapidity an assembly line foreman would admire. Regulations recommend a "thorough examination" with "an average of 15 minutes per examinee."

During this time, the evaluation of each registrant is supposed to cover items 18 through 41 of the Medical Examination Report (SF 88, see Appendix). Abnormalities are required to be noted for the head, face, neck, and scalp; nose, sinuses, mouth and throat; ears; eyes; chest and lungs; heart and vascular system; abdomen and gastrointestinal system; anus and rectum; endocrine system; genitourinary system: skin; spine; and upper and lower extremities.

In reality, the following is likely to occur. One doctor will go down the rows of examinees with a stethoscope, stopping at each registrant long enough to listen to two heartbeats. A second physician, beginning at the opposite end of the room, will wend his way up the rows, making the ear check. One ear, and then twenty-five examinees later, the other ear. Then lights out, and a doctor with a small flashlight performs the eye check, trotting down the lines, allowing the beam to probe no one pair of eyes for more than a few seconds. For the particularly short or tall, the "eye check" often turns out to be a scalp or shoulder examination. Meanwhile, a clerk with a clipboard hurries along behind, making notations.

After it has been determined that all registrants have two eyes, the same number of ears, and a heart, the chief examiner gives the "drop shorts" command. One hundred men bend over and spread their cheeks, while the doctors check for hemorrhoids.

There follows what is officially labeled the "orthopedic evaluation," to be done in groups of six "in the presence of an examining physician who will personally observe each examinee." Actually most often accomplished in groups of one hundred, the evaluation involves a series of movements and exercises designed to demonstrate, for the practiced eye (were it watching), the strength and range of motion in various limbs and joints.

All registrants, having been thus evaluated, file out to wait in line to provide a urine sample, a blood sample, and have their chests X-rayed. A check for venereal disease may also be made at this point (procedure: a sergeant yells out, "Hey, any of you guys have VD?"), but these three laboratory tests will always be done. If albumin, sugar, or blood cells are found in the urine, the examining physician may require a registrant to urinate in his presence and urinalysis is required to be repeated twice a day for three days.[10]

The third part of the medical examination involves the recording of measurements for height, weight, blood pressure, vision, and hearing. Regulations warn Army doctors to be "familiar with situations that result in spurious elevation" of blood pressure.

As in the urinalysis, a single finding cannot result in rejection, and all persons with high blood pressure must be rechecked twice a day for three consecutive days.[11] The eye test includes both a check for color blindness and for distant visual acuity. (Complete examination: *Q.* "Can you read line 9?" *A.* "No." *Pause.* "Okay, next!") The strength of glasses will be recorded according to the registrant's prescription, or, if he has none, through use of a lens-measuring instrument.[12]

Contrary to draft folklore, the psychiatric interview is not routine. Only those who have given the examiners reason to question their "emotional, social, or intellectual adequacy for military service" will be evaluated.[13] In practice this means that only registrants with letters from their own psychiatrists will be examined. The evaluation will, in many cases, be made by the chief medical officer rather than an Army psychiatrist. Regulations suggest that "any evidence of disorganized or unclear thinking, of unusual thought control, of undue suspiciousness or of apathy or 'strangeness'" be noted. "Depression, expansiveness, withdrawal, or marked anxiety," the guidelines continue, "out of keeping with the content of the interview will be carefully evaluated." Actually, the doctor is likely to ask only a few perfunctory questions before checking the box marked normal or the one marked abnormal on the medical report (SF 88, item 42).

A brief interview with a physician will be, for most youths, the last they see of the Armed Forces Examining and Entrance Station—until they are inducted. Those who had counted on a thorough examination uncovering some unknown defect will still be waiting for the "real checkup" to begin when told to get dressed. Only then are they likely to realize that the careless, random examination interspersed with the "orthopedic evaluation" exercises and the hemorrhoid check was the only medical attention that would be paid their head, face, neck and scalp; nose, sinuses, mouth and throat; ears; eyes; chest and lungs; heart, etc.

On the other hand, the remarkably casual physical inspection will let many with documented disabilities of a doubtful nature breathe a sigh of relief.

Presenting the unfitness claim should be a simple matter. The interviewing physician will ask the state of your health, your cue to display the note from your private doctor. It is highly unlikely that any effort will be made to further evaluate the nature of your unfitness, beyond a brief question-and-answer session. No special laboratory tests, X rays, encephalograms, electrocardiograms, or hematologic studies are probable. If the interviewing physician is a civilian, a second interview with an Army doctor is customary. But his questions are not likely to be either more extensive or more probing, as long as the doctor's letter is adequate.

Regulations do, however, authorize the Army examiners to retain any registrant for further observation—if necessary, to place him in a hospital for intensive study—and to call in either a military or civilian specialist.[14] In addition, where doubt exists as to whether a youth meets minimum fitness standards, the case will be turned over to the U.S. Army Recruiting Command Surgeon for final determination. "Cases of unusual or controversial nature" are handled by the Surgeon General's Office, Department of the Army. That any of these steps would be taken is quite improbable; a quick decision, qualified or disqualified, is the norm.

If found medically unacceptable under current standards (as shown in Chapter Two), regulations require that you be further evaluated under mobilization standards. This is to determine if you should be classified IV-F or I-Y. If unfit under current criteria but fit under mobilization standards, a I-Y rating is assigned; if below mobilization requirements, a IV-F exemption is granted. "This additional evaluation should be accomplished as carefully as the original," the Army instructs its examiners. Apparently the examiners take these directions seriously—the mobilization evaluation is so like the original that one is rarely aware it is being performed at all.

If you have a defect or condition listed as cause for rejection you cannot be inducted. Even if your ailment is remediable, you cannot be found qualified for service. "No individuals," regulations state, "will be accepted on a provisional basis subject to the successful treatment or correction of a disqualifying defect."[15]

Upon completion of the medical examination, the Army will assign Selective Service evaluation symbols to each registrant. These symbols—X: qualified; Y: currently disqualified; and Z: permanently disqualified—determine your precise draft classification. Your local board has no say in the process.

If found acceptable, the results of your physical are valid for one year. If you are not inducted within that time, a completely new physical of the same scope will be given. If ordered to induction before the one-year deadline, you will undergo a "physical inspection." Unless you can substantiate an unfitness claim previously ignored, or document a new claim, the induction inspection will be a rubber stamp certification of the preinduction physical.

And the next words you hear will be: "You are about to be inducted into the Armed Forces of the United States. . . . You will take one step forward as your name and service are called . . ."

7

Appeals, Discharges, Pensions

A STATEMENT OF ACCEPTABILITY IS NOT THE END
of the road. Even if found fit for military service at
your physical, your induction is far from inevitable.
Don't succumb to resignation or allow yourself to
be panicked into enlisting.

Since 1950, just a third of those examined and
found qualified have actually been inducted. In 1966,
the year of the highest draft calls since Korea, more
than a million men were certified fit, but only
366,000 received induction orders. And of those,
more than 26,000 were rejected at the induction
center for defects overlooked at their physicals.[1]

But if an adverse verdict from your physical is not
final, it is a distinct threat to your freedom. You can
be drafted at any time once determined acceptable,

and might well have as little as a month before asked to take that fateful one step forward. There is no time to waste, therefore, in challenging the results of your physical. The course is similar whether you failed to claim unfitness at the examination, could not back your claim with a doctor's letter, or had a documented claim rejected.

Before taking any action, consider the strength of your original bid for exemption. Perhaps your problem is not a physical defect, as you first believed, but really of a psychiatric nature (see Chapter Four). Do not assume, however, that a disability is not serious enough to be cause for rejection simply because a medical examiner at your physical so decided.

A medical appeal, unlike regular appeals of classification, does not delay induction. Therefore, it is important not only that you initiate the challenge quickly, but also that you simultaneously seek postponement of action by your local board through your State Director.

Any other moves which might hold off induction while the medical review is pending—such as unrelated appeals through normal Selective Service channels—should be attempted. After an induction notice has arrived, only a formal postponement will do. But a written request to your local board must be based on illness (doctor's note required), a death in the immediate family, or an "extreme emergency" beyond your control involving either yourself or your family. If granted, the postponement can be for a maximum of sixty days, but will usually be shorter.[2]

Official notification of the results of your physical will generally come within a month of the examination (Statement of Acceptability, DD 62). There will be no explanation if the box marked acceptable is checked unless you claimed a disability, in which case the following should appear:

> Registrant is determined acceptable; however, he claims ailments unverified by the medical officers and has been advised to present documentary evidence at his own expense to substantiate claims to his Selective Service local board prior to induction.

But whatever the form says—as long as it also says "acceptable"—follow the steps outlined below. If you simply send a doctor's letter to your board, there's a good chance no one will review it until you are called for induction. And if they reject it then, there's no time to appeal.

As soon as the form arrives, appeal by registered letter to:

The Surgeon
U.S. Army Recruiting Command
Hampton, Virginia 23369

The letter should include a description of your disqualifying condition, an explanation of why this condition was not discovered at your physical, and a request that you either be granted a new examination or be declared medically unacceptable. It must be accompanied by a note from your doctor.

The plea should reflect your concern for your health, physical or mental, and not your antipathy for military service. If your defect is one specifically listed, note the appropriate section of AR 40-501 (see Chapter Two); if not, some general provision of the standards might be cited.

The cursory nature of preinduction physicals, the failure of examiners to follow regulations, should make it easy to explain why your problem was overlooked. The shortcomings of the medical evaluation of your condition should be briefly described. If regulations were ignored, say so and cite the sections involved. Did you claim psychiatric unfitness? Note that you were not examined by a psychiatrist (if this was the case). Have lower back or leg pain? The mass orthopedic evaluation probably did not allow sufficient time for examination. If you did not have a doctor's letter at the time of your physical, but claimed a disability, you should have been told to obtain a physician's report. In that case, your appeal was actually advised by the Army. If you made no claim, explain why the condition described was not mentioned earlier.

Every registrant has the right to inspect his own draft file at his local board. If you had a physical, your file should include a Statement of Acceptability (DD 62), a Record of Induction (DD 47), the Report of Medical Examination (SF 88), and the Report of Medical History (SF 89).[3] Examine these records. It is your responsibility to ensure your file is complete, and the forms might provide material for your appeal.

Include at least your original doctor's letter in your appeal. But if this letter was presented at your physical and ignored, it quite possibly is not strong enough. Try to get something better for the second round, and perhaps seek the aid of a second doctor as well. If medical records—X-ray or laboratory reports—can be produced to document the diagnosis of your physician, these too should be forwarded.

If the first appeal is denied, your next letter goes to:

Chief, Physical Standards Division
Office of the Surgeon General
Department of the Army
Washington, D.C. 20315

Follow the same format as before, but be sure to note that the Surgeon, U.S. Army Recruiting Command, has already been notified and has declined to either reverse the finding of the physical or arrange a new examination. This procedure should be used regardless of how much time has passed since your physical.

Letters may also be sent to the medical adviser of your State Director and to the Director of Selective Service, and could result in re-examination. The Army route, however, is generally more effective.

If you went to your physical without a doctor's letter, your local board too should be on your mailing list. In addition to taking the steps outlined above, send the board a brief note and your physician's report. The board itself will probably take no action, but the papers will be forwarded to the examining station for evaluation by Army doctors or attached to induction medical records if the order has already been issued.

If, despite your best efforts, you are called for induction, your fate is still not sealed. Thousands of men report for service only to be sent home as civilian medical rejects. Before you can become a soldier, you must pass one last physical inspection.

Bring a copy of your doctor's letter to the induction center, regardless to whom you might already have sent it. Unless some specific disqualifying condition is brought to his attention, the Army examiner will perform only the prescribed examination: "The examinee, with clothing removed, will be closely observed to detect the presence of any communicable diseases and apparent defects not previously recorded." And that's it.

But regulations do require that the doctor note "any intervening injuries or illnesses, or other health problems not a matter of record" and further instruct that all documents presented be reviewed. Indeed, the examining physician must enter a signed "reviewed and considered" statement on all material.

Since eleventh-hour ailments are likely to be met with a degree of skepticism, your chances for a reprieve will be better if the condition was at least noted at your preinduction examination. But a last-minute claim is better than none at all.

Even after induction, your sentence to military duty can be commuted well before the full two years have been served. And you might leave the Army well paid for your time in uniform.

A soldier can be medically discharged if he:
* actually did not meet induction fitness standards even if qualified for continued service
* is unfit for retention in the Army due to a condition existing prior to induction
* is unfit for retention due to a condition incurred or aggravated while in uniform

Those discharged under the last circumstances will receive a disability pension. In other words, if you're drafted despite claimed unfitness and your problem is worsened by Army life, they have to redeem in cash what you forfeited in health.

It is, of course, much more difficult to get out of the Army than to stay out in the first place. But thousands are discharged with disqualifying defects missed at their physicals and thousands more are released with disabilities intensified by military duty.

The procedures for claiming unfitness after induction are complex, and it is not possible to provide a comprehensive account in this space. Your basic rights are outlined below, but at some point in the proceedings it will probably be necessary to rely on military counsel or retain a private attorney familiar with this field.

Your fitness for further military duty will normally be considered at three distinct levels: the base doctor who examines you on sick call, a panel of three doctors, and a board of three officers. Each successive step depends on your being found unfit at the previous level. If disability benefits are involved, the case will also be judged by a headquarters review council, whose decision, if challenged, will be considered by an appeals board.

The medical yardstick for deciding who is qualified to remain a soldier is different than that for determining who is acceptable to enter the service. While the induction standards (AR 40-501, Chapter Two) provide specific causes for rejection, the retention standards (AR 40-501, Chapter Three) provide only general guidelines, and having a listed defect does not mean automatic discharge. In addition, many conditions which would prevent your induction are not considered sufficient reason to turn in your khakis.

There is one provision in Army regulations, however, which allows new recruits to escape the barracks by successfully claiming that they were drafted in error. It provides, in effect, a second chance to appeal the results of your preinduction physical.

If you can show that you were unfit when accepted for induction with a disqualifying condition missed by the examiners, you will be sent home even before basic training is over. But you must submit a request for discharge to your unit commander within the first four months of active duty. After that, you can only get out if found unfit under the tougher retention standards.

Your case will be considered by a medical board composed of three or more military doctors appointed by the commander of the base hospital. "Eligibility for discharge will be governed," regulations state, "by a medical board finding that the individual has a medical condition which would have permanently disqualified him for entry in the military service had it been detected at that time."[4] (The criteria used are those printed in Chapter Two of this book.)

You will be given an opportunity to appear before the panel of physicians, and if their finding is adverse, submit any evidence (including a letter from a private physician) to the officer who must approve the board's decision. If the medical board supports your claim, you will be discharged within seventy-two hours, none the richer, but a free man.

The regular routine for obtaining a medical discharge will most likely begin with a long wait on sick call line outside the dispensary. Your sergeant might give you hell, but regulations actually require that a recruit "seek timely medical advice whenever he has reason to believe that he has a medical condition or a physical defect which affects, or is likely to affect, his physical or mental well-being."

The doctor should find you unfit if your physical or psychiatric condition would make continued performance of duty impossible, detrimental to your "health or well-being" or prejudicial to "the best interests of the Government." (The medical standards for retention can be obtained from the Government Printing Office, Washington, D.C. 20402; send $1.75 and ask for AR 40-501.)

If he believes you unfit, the doctor will turn your case over to a medical board, where three of his colleagues will reconsider whether you are qualified for further military service and also try to decide if the disability was incurred or aggravated by such service.

If the medical board determines that you are unfit due to a condition contracted while still a civilian which hasn't been aggravated by soldiering, you will be offered a quick discharge without disability benefits. If you accept the offer, you must give up any monetary claim against the Army and your right to a full hearing with legal representation. But you can still seek disability payments from the Veterans Administration later.[5]

Should you decline to apply for "expeditious discharge," you risk not being discharged at all. Your case will be treated like that of any other enlisted man found unfit by a medical board. It will be referred to a Physical Evaluation Board of three officers—only one of whom will be a doctor—which can reverse the findings of the first panel.

The PEB officers will hold an informal hearing, review the records, and decide: (*a*) if you are unfit;

(*b*) whether the disability was incurred in or aggravated by military service; (*c*) whether it is the result of "intentional misconduct or willful neglect"; (*d*) whether a pension should be awarded.

If you accept the PEB findings, your case will go directly to Army headquarters for final review. If you challenge them, a formal hearing will be convened by the PEB. It is your absolute right to demand such a hearing. You can either be represented by assigned military counsel or retain a private attorney. All records connected with the hearing will be open to your inspection. In addition, your lawyer can call witnesses, take dispositions, introduce evidence, and cross-examine all called to testify.[6]

The board will make its formal rulings in closed session by majority vote. You may either accept its decision or file a formal rebuttal to it. In either case, the PEB findings will be considered by the Army Physical Review Council, a panel of senior officers in the medical, legal, and personnel areas. Neither you nor your attorney can appear before the Council, which can revise PEB findings only when "there is compelling evidence" they are in error. If the Council simply upholds the PEB, its verdict is final.

Should it modify the PEB findings, you may challenge this action, and the case will go to the Office of the Secretary of the Army, where it will be handled by the Army Physical Disability Appeal Board. The master board can concur with the PEB, with the review council, with your rebuttal, or make its own disposition.[7]

When the dust has settled—if you haven't died of old age—you will either find yourself back in the barracks with your unfitness claim rejected, home without any cash for your troubles, or living happily ever after at the government's expense. At least you will have given everyone enough of a headache that when the next young man walks into his physical to claim his IV-F, they'll think twice before sending him an induction notice.

Bibliographical Note

THE MOST IMPORTANT SOURCES FOR THIS BOOK were the many physicians, psychiatrists, lawyers, and draft counselors who contributed their knowledge and experience in the course of numerous interviews. Listed here, however, are only those official and unofficial publications that would be useful to those faced with the draft who want more detailed information than is provided in this manual. There are no other comprehensive treatments of the unfitness question, and no attempt has been made to list the many books having some information in this area.

The most important publication to be consulted

is AR 40-501, *Standards of Medical Fitness*, available for $1.75 from:

Government Printing Office
Washington, D.C. 20402

In addition to the standards for induction printed in Chapter Two, AR 40-501 includes standards for retention, special criteria for physicians drafted, a detailed outline for military medical examiners, and other data. From time to time, the Army issues revisions (usually minor) of the standards. The information in this book is from AR 40-501 through change 25, 2 February, 1970. Further changes can be obtained from the GPO.

Other useful Army publications are AR 601-270, *Armed Forces Examining and Entrance Stations* (March 1969), which sets forth policy and procedures for administering preinduction and induction examinations, and AR 604-10, *Personnel Security Clearance* (November 1969), which outlines policy and procedures for investigating alleged subversives.

There are three sets of regulations covering the complex area of medical discharges and disability pensions: AR 635-40, *Physical Evaluation for Retention, Retirement, or Separation*; a few paragraphs of AR 635-200, *Personnel Separation: Enlisted Personnel,* involving erroneous induction; and AR 40-3, *Medical, Dental, and Veterinary Care*.

The above publications can be obtained at no cost through a telephone call to the supplies division of the Department of Defense in Washington (202 OX 5-2284) or by writing to:

U.S. Army Publications Center
2800 Eastern Blvd.
Baltimore, Maryland 21220

The security handbook, AR 604-10, is also available from:

Headquarters
Department of the Army
Office of the Adjutant General
Washington, D.C. 20315

For the registrant who wishes to know his legal rights under all aspects of the draft law, the best source of information is the *Selective Service Law Reporter,* published by the Public Law Education Institute in Washington (1346 Connecticut Ave. N.W.). Indispensable for lawyers in the field, it is an accurate, complete, sometimes technically worded guide and includes reprints of relevant regulations. It is available as a continually updated looseleaf service for $35 per year to nonprofit groups and students.

Official *Selective Service Regulations* (Section 1628 deals with physical examinations) can be obtained from the Government Printing Office for $5. You also get the Selective Service Act of 1967 as part of a package deal which includes future changes at no extra cost.

Also useful are *Local Board Memorandum No. 14,* "Procedures to be Followed When Registrant Refuses to Submit to Physical Examination," and *Operations Bulletin No. 327,* "Medical Interview by Local Board Medical Examiner."

The only published material dealing directly with medical unfitness are two articles published by the National Lawyers' Guild (Box 673, Berkeley, California 94701): Peter Franck, "Presenting Medical and Psychiatric Unfitness for Duty Under the Draft Law"; and Dr. Neal Blumenfeld, "Psychiatric Examinations and Reports on Draft Clients." Both are in the summer 1967 issue of the *Guild Practitioner*.

An interesting untitled pamphlet prepared as a guide for young doctors who wish to avoid military service is available from:

Boston Medical Resistance Union
c/o Medical Committee for Human Rights
Box 382, Prudential Station
Boston, Mass. 02199

The Central Committee for Conscientious Objectors (2016 Walnut Street, Philadelphia, Pennsylvania 19103) publishes a wide array of material for draft-liable youths, much of it concerning areas other than conscientious objection. Their August 1968 memorandum on the Security Questionnaire is useful but not comprehensive.

Most of the statistics quoted in this book are from the *Statistical Abstract of the United States: 1969* (89th edition), published by the U.S. Bureau of the Census in September 1968, or from the Medical Statistics Division of the Army Surgeon General's Office.

Footnotes

Introduction

1. For more extensive information see David E. Rosenbaum's "Questions and Answers on the Draft," *New York Times*, 4 December 1969, pp. 37, 44.

1/Rx for Resisters

1. *Selective Service Regulations*, sec. 1628.1.
2. *Standards of Medical Fitness*, AR 40-501, sec. 1-3 (*b*); see also *Selective Service Act of 1967*, sec. 4(*a*).
3. AR 40-501, sec. 1-2(*a*).
4. *Selective Service Regulations*, secs. 1628.25, 1628.4.
5. Ibid., sec. 1628.2(*b*).
6. Ibid., sec. 1628.5.
7. Ibid., sec. 1628.3(*a*).
8. Ibid., sec. 1628.4(*e*).

9. Ibid., sec. 1628.10.
10. Ibid., secs. 1628.12, 1632.2.
11. Ibid., sec. 1628.14.
12. AR 40-501, secs. 1-4, 10-14(*c*); 1-3(*b*).
13. *Selective Service Regulations,* sec. 1622.17.
14. Ibid., sec. 1622.44.
15. *Armed Forces Examining and Entrance Stations,* AR 601-270, sec. 4-22(*c*).

2/Medical Unfitness

1. AR 40-501, sec. 1-2(*a*).

3/The Gray Area

1. Peter Franck, "Presenting Medical and Psychiatric Unfitness for Duty Under the Draft Law," *Guild Practitioner* 26 (1967): 76.

4/Psychiatric Unfitness

1. Neal Blumenfeld, "Psychiatric Examinations and Reports on Draft Clients," *Guild Practitioner* 26 (1967): 74.
2. AR 601-270, sec. 4-20*h*(1-*b*).
3. Blumenfeld, op. cit., p. 71.
4. AR 601-270, sec. 4-20*h*(1-*b*).

5/Moral Unfitness

1. AR 601-270, secs. 3-8, 3-9. (All information from official regulations included in the criminal record section of this chapter comes from this source.)
2. Ibid., sec. 3-9*f*(1-*e*).
3. Ibid., app. D, sec. D-1.
4. Ibid., D-2.
5. Ibid., sec. 5-6*b*(3); see also *Personal Security Clearance,* AR 604-10, sec. 3-3(*c*).
6. AR 604-10, sec. 2-3, 2-4.
7. AR 601-270, app. I.

6/The Preinduction Physical

1. U.S., Bureau of the Census, *Statistical Abstract of the United States*, 89th ed. (1968), is the source for all of the figures cited; tables 383, 385, and 387 are especially useful.
2. "Draft Director Tells What's Ahead," *U.S. News & World Report*, vol. 60, no. 2 (10 January 1966), pp. 41–42.
3. *Selective Service Regulations*, sec. 1628.17(*f*).
4. *Local Board Memorandum No. 14*, sec. 3(*b, c*).
5. AR 40-501, sec. 10-15(*d*-1).
6. AR 601-270, sec. 4-22 *d*.
7. Ibid., sec. 4-10*a*(2); app. I, sec. 1-5(*b*).
8. Ibid., sec. 4-11.
9. *Statistical Abstract* (1968), table 385.
10. AR 40-501, sec. 11-19(*c*).
11. Ibid., sec. 11-10(*a*-4).
12. AR 601-270, sec. 4-20*h*(3-*d*).
13. Ibid., sec. 4-20*h*(1-*b*).
14. Ibid., sec. 4-20*h*(5); AR 40-501, sec. 10-4.
15. AR 40-501, sec. 1-3(*a*).

7/Appeals, Discharges, Pensions

1. *Statistical Abstract* (1968), tables 376, 385; and information from Army Surgeon General's Office.
2. *Selective Service Regulations*, sec. 1632.2.
3. Ibid., sec. 1628.25(*d*).
4. *Personnel Separation: Enlisted Personnel*, AR 635-200, sec. 5-9.
5. *Physical Evaluation for Retention, Retirement, or Separation*, AR 635-40, chap. 9.
6. Ibid., chap. 4.
7. Ibid., chap. 5.

Appendixes

Appendix 1
ORDER TO REPORT
FOR PHYSICAL
(SSS 223)

SELECTIVE SERVICE SYSTEM

Approval Not Required.

ORDER TO REPORT FOR
ARMED FORCES PHYSICAL EXAMINATION

To

_____
(LOCAL BOARD STAMP)

....
(Date of mailing)

SELECTIVE SERVICE NO.

You are hereby directed to present yourself for Armed Forces Physical Examination by reporting
at:

. . . .
(Place of reporting)

on .... at ....
(Date) (Hour)

....
(Member or clerk of Local Board)

IMPORTANT NOTICE
(Read Each Paragraph Carefully)

TO ALL REGISTRANTS:

When you report pursuant to this order you will be forwarded to an Armed Forces Examining Station where it will be determined whether you are qualified for military service under current standards. Upon completion of your examination, you will be returned to the place of reporting designated above. It is possible that you may be retained at the Examining Station for more than 1 day for the purpose of further testing or for medical consultation. You will be furnished transportation, and meals and lodging when necessary, from the place of reporting designated above to the Examining Station and return. Following your examination your local board will mail you a statement issued by the commanding officer of the station showing whether you are qualified for military service under current standards.

If you are employed, you should inform your employer of this order and that the examination is merely to determine whether you are qualified for military service. To protect your right to return to your job, you must report for work as soon as possible after the completion of your examination. You may jeopardize your reemployment rights if you do not report for work at the beginning of your next regularly scheduled working period after you have returned to your place of employment.

IF YOU HAVE HAD PREVIOUS MILITARY SERVICE, OR ARE NOW A MEMBER OF THE NATIONAL GUARD OR A RESERVE COMPONENT OF THE ARMED FORCES, BRING EVIDENCE WITH YOU. IF YOU WEAR GLASSES, BRING THEM. IF MARRIED, BRING PROOF OF YOUR MARRIAGE. IF YOU HAVE ANY PHYSICAL OR MENTAL CONDITION WHICH, IN YOUR OPINION, MAY DISQUALIFY YOU FOR SERVICE IN THE ARMED FORCES, BRING A PHYSICIAN'S CERTIFICATE DESCRIBING THAT CONDITION, IF NOT ALREADY FURNISHED TO YOUR LOCAL BOARD.

If you are so far from your own Local Board that reporting in compliance with this Order will be a hardship and you desire to report to the Local Board in the area in which you are now located, take this Order and go immediately to that Local Board and make written request for transfer for examination.

TO CLASS I-A AND I-A-O REGISTRANTS:

If you fail to report for examination as directed, you may be declared delinquent and ordered to report for induction into the Armed Forces. You will also be subject to fine and imprisonment under the provisions of the Universal Military Training and Service Act, as amended.

TO CLASS I-O REGISTRANTS:

This examination is given for the purpose of determining whether you are qualified for military service. If you are found qualified, you will be available, in lieu of induction, to be ordered to perform civilian work contributing to the maintenance of the national health, safety or interest. If you fail to report for or to submit to this examination, you will be subject to be ordered to perform civilian work in the same manner as if you had taken the examination and had been found qualified for military service.

SSS Form 223 (Revised 11-13-65) (Previous printings may be used until exhausted.)

U.S. GOVERNMENT PRINTING OFFICE: 1966—O-764-954

138

Appendix 2
ORDER TO APPEAR
FOR MEDICAL INTERVIEW
(SSS 219)

SELECTIVE SERVICE SYSTEM

Approval
Not Required

NOTICE TO REGISTRANT TO APPEAR FOR MEDICAL INTERVIEW

(Local Board Stamp)

Date of mailing

(Month) (Day) (Year)

Selective Service No.

You are hereby directed to report for a medical interview at the place and time designated below:

....
(Place of reporting)

on .... at ....
(Date)   (Hour)

....
(Member or clerk of Local Board)

SAMPLE

IMPORTANT NOTICE

This medical interview will be of a preliminary nature, for the purpose of disclosing those obvious defects or manifest conditions which would disqualify you for service in the armed forces, and will not finally determine your acceptability for military service. Should you be found to have no obviously disqualifying defects you will be ordered to report for an Armed Forces Physical Examination.

If you are so far from the place designated above that reporting in compliance with this Notice will be a hardship, take this Notice immediately to the local board for the area in which you are now located and make written request for a transfer for medical interview.

Failure to comply with this Notice will result in your being declared a delinquent and subject to the penalties provided by the Universal Military Training and Service Act.

SSS FORM NO. 219   (Revised 2-6-64)   (Previous printings may be used)   U S GOVERNMENT PRINTING OFFICE 1964 OF—721-518

Appendix 3

RECORD OF INDUCTION (DD 47)

RECORD OF INDUCTION (Local Board Will Prepare From Latest Information Available)

Form Approved
Budget Bureau No.22-R082.6

DO NOT DEFACE THIS STAMP

(Local Board of Origin Stamp)

SECTION I - GENERAL

1. LAST NAME - FIRST NAME - MIDDLE NAME

2. SERVICE NUMBER (To be entered by Induction Station)

3. HOME OF RECORD (Number and street or rural route - if none no state - city or post office, county and state) (To be entered by Induction Station)

3a. CURRENT ADDRESS

4. SELECTIVE SERVICE NUMBER

5. DATE OF BIRTH
DAY	MONTH	YEAR

6. MARITAL STATUS
- [ ] SINGLE
- [ ] MARRIED
- [ ] DIVORCED
- [ ] WIDOWED

7.

DEPENDENTS

7. NO. CHILDREN UNDER 18

7a. OTHER DEPENDENTS (Exclusive of wife, if married, and children indicated in item 7d)

8a.

PRIOR MILITARY SERVICE [ ] YES [ ] NO (If "Yes", Complete Items Below)

8. SERVICE NUMBER

8b. DATE OF ENL., IND., APT AND/OR ORDER TO ACTIVE DUTY

8f. DATE OF DISCHARGE OR RELEASE

8a. COMPONENT
- [ ] REGULAR
- [ ] US
- [ ] RES
- [ ] NG

8c. CHARACTER OF DISCHARGE OR SERVICE

8h. REASON AND AUTHORITY FOR DISCHARGE OR RELEASE (Cite appropriate service regulation)

8a. ARMED FORCE
- [ ] ARMY
- [ ] NAVY
- [ ] AIR FORCE
- [ ] MARINE CORPS
- [ ] COAST GUARD

9a. PRESENT CIVILIAN TRADE OR OCCUPATION (Type of business)

9. LENGTH OF EXPERIENCE
YEARS	MONTHS

10.

EDUCATION

10. GRADE OR YEAR COMPLETED (Line through all grades or years successfully completed) (Exclude trade or business schools)

ELEMENTARY AND HIGH SCHOOL
NONE	1	2	3	4	5	6	7	8	9	10	11	12

COLLEGE
1	2	3	4

POST GRADUATE
1	2	3	4

10a. U.S. CITIZEN
- [ ] YES
- [ ] NO

IF NOT A U.S. CITIZEN

11. PLACE OF BIRTH

11a. DATE OF ENTRY INTO U.S. FOR
- [ ] PERMANENT
- [ ] TEMPORARY RESIDENCE

11b. ALIEN REGISTRATION RECEIPT CARD NUMBER

11c. FOREIGN COUNTRY OF WHICH CITIZEN

12. IF NATURALIZED CITIZEN, GIVE DATE, PLACE, COURT OF JURISDICTION AND NATURALIZATION NUMBER

15A. CONVICTED OR ADJUDICATED OF CRIME OTHER THAN MINOR TRAFFIC VIOLATION (If "Yes", specify nature, date, location of court and sentence)
☐ YES ☐ NO

4. NOW IN CUSTODY OF LAW
☐ YES ☐ NO
IF ANSWER TO "ITEM 4" IS NECESSARY RELEASE OR WAIVER ATTACHED?
☐ YES ☐ NO

16. CONSCIENTIOUS OBJECTOR
☐ CLASS I-O
☐ CLASS I-O

15. PREVIOUSLY EXAMINED AND NOT ACCEPTABLE (Check one)
☐ YES ☐ NO (If "Yes", indicate the following)
☐ NOT ACCEPTABLE ON PREINDUCTION ☐ NOT ACCEPTABLE ON INDUCTION ☐ NOT ACCEPTABLE ON ENLISTMENT

SECTION II - LOCAL BOARD MEDICAL INTERVIEW

16.

PHYSICAL DEFECTS
(To be completed
by Local Board)

A. LIST ALL DEFECTS AND DISEASES CLAIMED BY THE REGISTRANT AND ANY DEFECTS OR DISEASES WHICH THE REGISTRANT MAY HAVE, AND WHICH ARE KNOWN TO THE LOCAL BOARD (If in doubt, indicate by "Doer")

B. ARE ANY OF THE DEFECTS OR DISEASES LISTED IN ITEM "A" ABOVE INCLUDED IN LIST OF DEFECTS (Par 1069, SS Reg)? ☐ YES ☐ NO

C. REGISTRANT OR AFFIDAVIT REFERRED TO LOCAL BOARD MEDICAL ADVISOR ☐ YES ☐ NO

17.   STATEMENT OF LOCAL BOARD MEDICAL ADVISOR (To be Completed if Item 16-C is "Yes")

FINDING:
A. ☐ REGISTRANT DOES NOT HAVE DISQUALIFYING DEFECT(S) CLAIMED

B. ☐ REGISTRANT HAS THE FOLLOWING DISQUALIFYING DEFECT OR DISEASE (Specify the principal disqualifying defect first, list all other defects in order of significance, and attach affidavits or statements)

C. REMARKS

DATE	PLACE	SIGNATURE OF LOCAL BOARD MEDICAL ADVISOR (When Item 16c is "Yes")
		SIGNATURE OF MEMBER OR CLERK OF LOCAL BOARD (When Item 16c is "Yes")

DD FORM 47
1 NOV 58   PREVIOUS EDITION OF THIS FORM ARE OBSOLETE.

(Appendix 3 continued pp. 142-43.)

(*Appendix 3 continued.*)

SECTIONS III THROUGH X OF THIS FORM WILL BE FILLED OUT AT INDUCTION STATION

SECTION III - MEDICAL DETERMINATION

NOTE: Changes in physical profile or physical category will be entered on separate lines under original determination.

18.								PHYSICAL CATEGORY				
DATE	PHYSICAL PROFILE - SERIAL						A	B	C	D	E
	P	U	L	H	E	S						

SECTION IV - ORDER OF REGISTRANTS SERVICE PREFERENCE

19. PLACE ORDER OF PREFERENCE NUMBER IN BOX

ARMY ☐   NAVY ☐
MARINE CORPS ☐   COAST GUARD ☐
AIR FORCE ☐   NONE ☐

SECTION V - MENTAL DETERMINATION

20a. TEST - FORM - SCORE	APTI MENTAL GROUP	I	II	III	IV	V	☐ ADMINISTRATIVELY ACCEPTED
20b. OTHER TEST(S)							SCORE _____
							☐ QUALIFYING ☐ NONQUALIFYING

SECTION VI - MORAL DETERMINATION

21. REGISTRANT HAS BEEN PERSONALLY INTERVIEWED AT TIME OF:

a. ☐ PREINDUCTION - REVEALED COURT ADJUDICATION OR CONVICTION ☐ YES* ☐ NO   WAIVER: ☐ NOT REQUIRED ☐ GRANTED ☐ NOT GRANTED ☐ NOT PROCEEDED

b. ☐ INDUCTION - REVEALED COURT ADJUDICATION OR CONVICTION ☐ YES* ☐ NO   WAIVER: ☐ NOT REQUIRED ☐ GRANTED ☐ NOT GRANTED ☐ NOT PROCEEDED

*Except minor traffic violations.   REMARKS:

SECTION VII - DETERMINATION AT PREINDUCTION EXAMINATION

22. THE QUALIFICATIONS OF THE ABOVE NAMED REGISTRANT HAVE BEEN CONSIDERED IN ACCORDANCE WITH THE CURRENT REGULATIONS GOVERNING THE ACCEPTANCE OF SELECTIVE SERVICE REGISTRANTS AND HE HAS THIS DATE:

a. ☐ FOUND ACCEPTABLE FOR INDUCTION INTO THE ARMED FORCES

b. ☐ FOUND NOT ACCEPTABLE FOR INDUCTION INTO THE ARMED FORCES FOR THE FOLLOWING REASONS:

ADMINISTRATIVE: ☐ NORMAL   ☐ ALIEN   ☐ OTHER ADMINISTRATIVE (Specify)
☐ TRAINABILITY LIMITED (Y=D)   ☐ FAILED APGT AND MEDICAL
☐ FAILED APGT ONLY   ☐ PSYCHIATRIC   ☐ OTHER MEDICAL.
FAILED MEDICAL ONLY: ☐ PSYCHIATRIC   ☐ OTHER MEDICAL.

DATE	PLACE	
TYPED NAME, NAME, GRADE, AND ORGANIZATION OF CO OF INDUCTION STATION		SIGNATURE

142

SECTION VIII - DETERMINATION AT INDUCTION EXAMINATION

33. TYPE OF EXAMINATION (Check one):
☐ PHYSICAL INSPECTION ☐ COMPLETE MEDICAL EXAMINATION (Done on basis of records) ☐ COMPLETE MEDICAL AND MENTAL EXAMINATION (Delinquents, parolees, volunteers, etc.)

a. ☐ FOUND ACCEPTABLE FOR INDUCTION b. ☐ FOUND NOT ACCEPTABLE FOR INDUCTION INTO THE ARMED FORCES FOR THE FOLLOWING REASONS:
   INTO THE ARMED FORCES
   ADMINISTRATIVE: ☐ PENAL ☐ ALIEN ☐ OTHER ADMINISTRATIVE (Specify):
                   ☐ TRAINABILITY LIMITED (T=0)
                   ☐ FAILED APDT ONLY ☐ FAILED APDT AND MEDICAL
   FAILED MEDICAL ONLY: ☐ PSYCHIATRIC ☐ OTHER MEDICAL

DATE	PLACE	SIGNATURE

TYPED NAME, GRADE AND ORGANIZATION OF CO OF INDUCTION STATION

SECTION IX - DISPOSITION OF INDUCTEE BY ARMED FORCES

34. THE QUALIFICATIONS OF THE ABOVE-NAMED INDIVIDUAL HAVE BEEN CONSIDERED IN ACCORDANCE WITH CURRENT REGULATIONS GOVERNING THE ACCEPTANCE OF SELECTIVE SERVICE REGISTRANTS AND HE HAS INDUCTED INTO:

☐ ARMY ☐ NAVY ☐ MARINE CORPS ☐ COAST GUARD ☐ AIR FORCE   e. DATE OF INDUCTION

AND ORDERED TO REPORT TO:

b. ORGANIZATION	c. LOCATION	d. DATE

d. INDUCTION STATION AT WHICH INDUCTED

TYPED OR STAMPED NAME AND GRADE OF INDUCTION OFFICER   SIGNATURE OF INDUCTION OFFICER

SECTION X - FINGERPRINTS OF RIGHT HAND (Fingerprint impressions will be made in this space in the case of every person inducted)

1. THUMB	2. INDEX	3. MIDDLE	4. RING	5. LITTLE

SAMPLE

Appendix 4

REPORT OF MEDICAL EXAMINATION (SF 88)

(Rev. June 1916)
Bureau of the Budget
Circular A-32 (Rev.)

88-109-04

REPORT OF MEDICAL EXAMINATION

1. LAST NAME—FIRST NAME—MIDDLE NAME	2. GRADE AND COMPONENT OR POSITION	3. IDENTIFICATION NO.
4. HOME ADDRESS (Number, street or R.F.D., city or town, zone and State)	5. PURPOSE OF EXAMINATION	6. DATE OF EXAMINATION

7. SEX	8. RACE	9. TOTAL YEARS GOVERNMENT SERVICE		10. AGENCY	11. ORGANIZATION UNIT
		MILITARY	CIVILIAN		
12. DATE OF BIRTH	13. PLACE OF BIRTH			14. NAME, RELATIONSHIP, AND ADDRESS OF NEXT OF KIN	

15. EXAMINING FACILITY OR EXAMINER, AND ADDRESS	16. OTHER INFORMATION

17. RATING OR SPECIALTY	TIME IN THIS CAPACITY (Total)	LAST SIX MONTHS

NOTES: (Describe every abnormality in detail. Enter pertinent item number before each comment. Continue in item 73 and use additional sheets if necessary.)

CLINICAL EVALUATION

NOR-MAL	(Check each item in appropriate column—enter "NE" if not evaluated.)	ABNOR-MAL	
	18. HEAD, FACE, NECK, AND SCALP		
	19. NOSE		
	20. SINUSES		
	21. MOUTH AND THROAT		
	22. EARS—GENERAL (Int. & ext. canals) (Auditory acuity under items 70 and 71)		
	23. DRUMS (Perforation)		
	24. EYES—GENERAL (Visual acuity and refraction under items 69, 60 and 67)		
	25. OPHTHALMOSCOPIC		
	26. PUPILS (Equality and reaction)		
	27. OCULAR MOTILITY (Associated parallel movements, nystagmus)		
	28. LUNGS AND CHEST (Include breasts)		

29. HEART (Thrust, size, rhythm, sounds)

30. VASCULAR SYSTEM (Varicosities, etc.)

31. ABDOMEN AND VISCERA (Include hernia)

32. ANUS AND RECTUM (Hemorrhoids, fistulae) (Prostate, if indicated)

33. ENDOCRINE SYSTEM

34. G-U SYSTEM

35. UPPER EXTREMITIES (Strength, range of motion)

36. FEET

37. LOWER EXTREMITIES (Except feet) (Strength, range of motion)

38. SPINE, OTHER MUSCULOSKELETAL

39. IDENTIFYING BODY MARKS, SCARS, TATTOOS

40. SKIN, LYMPHATICS

41. NEUROLOGIC (Equilibrium tests under item 72)

42. PSYCHIATRIC (Specify any personality deviation?)

43. PELVIC (Females only) (Check how done). ☐ VAGINAL ☐ RECTAL

REMARKS AND ADDITIONAL DENTAL DEFECTS AND DISEASES

(Continue in item 73)

44. DENTAL (Place appropriate symbols above or below number of upper and lower teeth, respectively.)

O—Restorable teeth
/—Nonrestorable teeth

X—Missing teeth
XXX—Replaced by dentures

(6 X 6)—Fixed bridge, brackets to include abutments

R	1	2	3	4	5	6	7	8	9	10	11	12	13	14	15	16	L
I-G-H-T	32	31	30	29	28	27	26	25	24	23	22	21	20	19	18	17	E-F-T

LABORATORY FINDINGS

45. URINALYSIS: A. SPECIFIC GRAVITY

B. ALBUMIN

C. SUGAR

D. MICROSCOPIC

46. EKG

49. BLOOD TYPE AND RH FACTOR

44. CHEST X-RAY (Place, date, film number and result)

47. SEROLOGY (Specify test used and result)

50. OTHER TESTS

(Appendix 4 continued pp. 146–47.)

145

(Appendix 4 continued.)

MEASUREMENTS AND OTHER FINDINGS

51. HEIGHT	52. WEIGHT	53. COLOR HAIR	54. COLOR EYES	55. BUILD (Check one)					56. TEMPERATURE
				SLENDER	MEDIUM	HEAVY	OBESE		

57.

BLOOD PRESSURE (Arm at heart level)					PULSE (Arm at heart level)			
A SITTING		B RECUM-BENT		C STANDING (3 min.)	A SITTING	B. AFTER EXERCISE	C 2 MIN. AFTER	D. RECUMBENT	E. AFTER STANDING 3 MIN
SYS	DIAS	SYS	DIAS	SYS	DIAS				

58.

59. DISTANT VISION		REFRACTION		NEAR VISION
RIGHT 20/	60.	S.	CX	61. CORR. TO BY
LEFT 20/	60. CORR. TO 20/ BY	S.	CX	CORR. TO BY

62. HETEROPHORIA (Specify distance)

ES°	EX°	R. H.	L. H.	PRISM DIV.	PRISM CONV. CT	PC	PO

63. ACCOMMODATION		64. COLOR VISION (Test used and result)	65. DEPTH PERCEPTION (Test used and score)		UNCORRECTED
RIGHT	LEFT				CORRECTED

66. FIELD OF VISION	67. NIGHT VISION (Test used and score)	68. RED LENS TEST	69. INTRAOCULAR TENSION

70. HEARING			71. AUDIOMETER								72. PSYCHOLOGICAL AND PSYCHOMOTOR (Tests used and score)
				250	500	1000	2000	3000	4000	6000	8000
				100	113	1002	1013	1023	1044	1144	1170
RIGHT WV	/15 SV	/15	RIGHT								
LEFT WV	/15 SV	/15	LEFT								

73. NOTES (Continued) AND SIGNIFICANT OR INTERVAL HISTORY

74. SUMMARY OF DEFECTS AND DIAGNOSES *(Use additional sheets if necessary)*

75. RECOMMENDATIONS—FURTHER SPECIALIST EXAMINATIONS INDICATED *(Specify)*

76. A. PHYSICAL PROFILE

	P	U	L	H	E	S

B. PHYSICAL CATEGORY

A	B	C	D	E

77. EXAMINEE *(Check)*

A. ☐ IS QUALIFIED FOR

B. ☐ IS NOT QUALIFIED FOR

78. IF NOT QUALIFIED, LIST DISQUALIFYING DEFECTS BY ITEM NUMBER

79. TYPED OR PRINTED NAME OF PHYSICIAN — SIGNATURE

80. TYPED OR PRINTED NAME OF PHYSICIAN — SIGNATURE

81. TYPED OR PRINTED NAME OF DENTIST OR PHYSICIAN *(Indicate which)* — SIGNATURE

82. TYPED OR PRINTED NAME OF REVIEWING OFFICER OR APPROVING AUTHORITY — SIGNATURE

NUMBER OF ATTACHED SHEETS

REPORT OF MEDICAL HISTORY (SF 89)

Standard Form 89
(Rev. March 1965)
Bureau of the Budget
Circular A-32

89-105-01

REPORT OF MEDICAL HISTORY

THIS INFORMATION IS FOR OFFICIAL USE ONLY AND WILL NOT BE RELEASED TO UNAUTHORIZED PERSONS

1. LAST NAME—FIRST NAME—MIDDLE NAME	2. GRADE AND COMPONENT OR POSITION	3. IDENTIFICATION NO.

4. HOME ADDRESS *(Number, street or RFD, city or town, State and ZIP Code)*	5. PURPOSE OF EXAMINATION	6. DATE OF EXAMINATION

7. SEX	8. RACE	9. TOTAL YEARS GOVERNMENT SERVICE		10. AGENCY	11. ORGANIZATION UNIT
		MILITARY	CIVILIAN		

12. DATE OF BIRTH	13. PLACE OF BIRTH	14. NAME, RELATIONSHIP, AND ADDRESS OF NEXT OF KIN

15. EXAMINING FACILITY OR EXAMINER, AND ADDRESS

16. OTHER INFORMATION

17. STATEMENT OF EXAMINEE'S PRESENT HEALTH IN OWN WORDS *(Follow by description of past history, if complaint exists)*

18. FAMILY HISTORY					19. HAS ANY BLOOD RELATION *(Parent, brother, sister, other)* OR HUSBAND OR WIFE			
RELATION	AGE	STATE OF HEALTH	IF DEAD, CAUSE OF DEATH	AGE AT DEATH	*(Check each item)*	YES	NO	RELATION(S)
FATHER					HAD TUBERCULOSIS			
MOTHER					HAD SYPHILIS			
SPOUSE					HAD DIABETES			
BROTHERS AND SISTERS					HAD CANCER			
					HAD KIDNEY TROUBLE			
					HAD HEART TROUBLE			
					HAD STOMACH TROUBLE			
					HAD RHEUMATISM *(Arthritis)*			
CHILDREN					HAD ASTHMA, HAY FEVER, HIVES			
					HAD EPILEPSY *(Fits)*			
					COMMITTED SUICIDE			

20. HAVE YOU EVER HAD OR HAVE YOU NOW (Place check at left of each item)

YES	NO	(Check each item)	YES	NO	(Check each item)	YES	NO	(Check each item)	YES	NO	(Check each item)
		SCARLET FEVER, ERYSIPELAS			GOITER			TUMOR, GROWTH, CYST, CANCER			"TRICK" OR LOCKED KNEE
		DIPHTHERIA			TUBERCULOSIS			RUPTURE/HERNIA			FOOT TROUBLE
		RHEUMATIC FEVER			SOAKING SWEATS (Night sweats)			APPENDICITIS			NEURITIS
		SWOLLEN OR PAINFUL JOINTS			ASTHMA			PILES OR RECTAL DISEASE			PARALYSIS (Inc. infantile)
		MUMPS			SHORTNESS OF BREATH			FREQUENT OR PAINFUL URINATION			EPILEPSY OR FITS
		COLOR BLINDNESS			PAIN OR PRESSURE IN CHEST			KIDNEY STONE OR BLOOD IN URINE			CAR, TRAIN, SEA, OR AIR SICKNESS
		FREQUENT OR SEVERE HEADACHE			CHRONIC COUGH			SUGAR OR ALBUMIN IN URINE			FREQUENT TROUBLE SLEEPING
		DIZZINESS OR FAINTING SPELLS			PALPITATION OR POUNDING HEART			BOILS			FREQUENT OR TERRIFYING NIGHTMARES
		EYE TROUBLE			HIGH OR LOW BLOOD PRESSURE			VD-SYPHILIS, GONORRHEA, ETC.			DEPRESSION OR EXCESSIVE WORRY
		EAR, NOSE OR THROAT TROUBLE			CRAMPS IN YOUR LEGS			RECENT GAIN OR LOSS OF WEIGHT			LOSS OF MEMORY OR AMNESIA
		RUNNING EARS			FREQUENT INDIGESTION			ARTHRITIS OR RHEUMATISM			BED WETTING
		HEARING LOSS			STOMACH, LIVER OR INTESTINAL TROUBLE			BONE, JOINT, OR OTHER DEFORMITY			NERVOUS TROUBLE OF ANY SORT
		CHRONIC OR FREQUENT COLDS			GALL BLADDER TROUBLE OR GALL STONES			LAMENESS			ANY DRUG OR NARCOTIC HABIT
		SEVERE TOOTH OR GUM TROUBLE			JAUNDICE			LOSS OF ARM, LEG, FINGER, OR TOE			EXCESSIVE DRINKING HABIT
		SINUSITIS			ANY REACTION TO SERUM, DRUG OR MEDICINE			PAINFUL OR "TRICK" SHOULDER OR ELBOW			HOMOSEXUAL TENDENCIES
		HAY FEVER			HISTORY OF BROKEN BONES			RECURRENT BACK PAIN			PERIODS OF UNCONSCIOUSNESS
		HISTORY OF HEAD INJURY										
		SKIN DISEASES										

21. HAVE YOU EVER (Check each item) | **22. FEMALES ONLY: A. HAVE YOU EVER —** | **B. COMPLETE THE FOLLOWING:**

YES	NO	(Check each item)	YES	NO			
		WORN GLASSES—CONTACT LENS			BEEN PREGNANT		AGE AT ONSET OF MENSTRUATION
		WORN AN ARTIFICIAL EYE			ATTEMPTED SUICIDE		INTERVAL BETWEEN PERIODS
		WORN HEARING AIDS			BEEN A SLEEP WALKER · HAD A VAGINAL DISCHARGE		DURATION OF PERIODS
		STUTTERED OR STAMMERED			LIVED WITH ANYONE WHO HAD TUBERCULOSIS · BEEN TREATED FOR A FEMALE DISORDER		DATE OF LAST PERIOD
		WORN A BRACE OR BACK SUPPORT			COUGHED UP BLOOD · HAD PAINFUL MENSTRUATION		QUANTITY: ☐ NORMAL ☐ EXCESSIVE ☐ SCANTY
					BLED EXCESSIVELY AFTER INJURY OR TOOTH EXTRACTION · HAD IRREGULAR MENSTRUATION		26. ARE YOU (Check one) ☐ RIGHT HANDED ☐ LEFT HANDED

23. HOW MANY JOBS HAVE YOU HAD IN THE PAST THREE YEARS?

24. WHAT IS THE LONGEST PERIOD YOU HELD ANY OF THESE JOBS? MONTHS

25. WHAT IS YOUR USUAL OCCUPATION?

(Appendix 5 continued pp. 150-51.)

(*Appendix 5 continued.*)

YES	NO	CHECK EACH ITEM YES OR NO. EVERY ITEM CHECKED "YES" MUST BE FULLY EXPLAINED IN BLANK SPACE ON RIGHT	
		27. HAVE YOU BEEN REFUSED EMPLOYMENT OR BEEN UNABLE TO HOLD A JOB BECAUSE OF: A. SENSITIVITY TO CHEMICALS, DUST, SUNLIGHT, ETC.	
		B. INABILITY TO PERFORM CERTAIN MOTIONS	
		C. INABILITY TO ASSUME CERTAIN POSITIONS	
		D. OTHER MEDICAL REASONS (*if yes, give reasons*)	
		28. HAVE YOU EVER WORKED WITH RADIOACTIVE SUBSTANCE?	
		29. DID YOU HAVE DIFFICULTY WITH SCHOOL STUDIES OR TEACHERS? (*If yes, give details*)	
		30. HAVE YOU EVER BEEN DENIED LIFE INSURANCE? (*If yes, state reason and give details*)	
		31. HAVE YOU HAD, OR HAVE YOU BEEN ADVISED TO HAVE, ANY OPERATIONS? (*If yes, describe and give age at which occurred*)	
		32. HAVE YOU EVER BEEN A PATIENT (*Committed or voluntary*) IN A MENTAL HOSPITAL OR SANITORIUM? (*If yes, specify when, where, why, and name of doctor, and complete address of hospital or clinic*)	
		33. HAVE YOU EVER HAD ANY ILLNESS OR INJURY OTHER THAN THOSE ALREADY NOTED? (*If yes, specify when, where, and give details*)	
		34. HAVE YOU CONSULTED OR BEEN TREATED BY CLINICS, PHYSICIANS, HEALERS, OR OTHER PRACTITIONERS WITHIN THE PAST 5 YEARS? (*If yes, give complete address of doctor, hospital, clinic, and details*)	
		35. HAVE YOU TREATED YOURSELF FOR ILLNESSES OTHER THAN MINOR COLDS? (*If yes, which illnesses*)	
		36. HAVE YOU EVER BEEN REJECTED FOR MILITARY SERVICE BECAUSE OF PHYSICAL, MENTAL, OR OTHER REASONS? (*If yes, give date and reason for rejection*)	

(1) yes, give date, reason, and type of discharge; whether honorable, other than honorable, for unfitness or unsuitability).

38. HAVE YOU EVER RECEIVED, IS THERE PENDING, OR HAVE YOU APPLIED FOR PENSION OR COMPENSATION FOR EXISTING DISABILITY? *(If yes, specify what kind, granted by whom, and what amount, when, why).*

WARNING   A FALSE OR DISHONEST ANSWER TO ANY OF THE QUESTIONS ON THIS FORM MAY BE PUNISHED BY FINE OR IMPRISONMENT (18 U.S.C. 1001).

I CERTIFY THAT I HAVE REVIEWED THE FOREGOING INFORMATION SUPPLIED BY ME AND THAT IT IS TRUE AND COMPLETE TO THE BEST OF MY KNOWLEDGE.
I AUTHORIZE ANY OF THE DOCTORS, HOSPITALS, OR CLINICS MENTIONED ABOVE TO FURNISH THE GOVERNMENT A COMPLETE TRANSCRIPT OF MY MEDICAL RECORD FOR PURPOSES OF PROCESSING MY APPLICATION FOR THIS EMPLOYMENT OR SERVICE.

TYPED OR PRINTED NAME OF EXAMINEE	SIGNATURE

39. PHYSICIAN'S SUMMARY AND ELABORATION OF ALL PERTINENT DATA *(Physician shall comment on all positive answers in items 20 thru 38.)*

TYPED OR PRINTED NAME OF PHYSICIAN OR EXAMINER	DATE	SIGNATURE	NUMBER OF ATTACHED SHEETS

☆ U.S. GOVERNMENT PRINTING OFFICE: 1966 OF—212-221

ARMED FORCES SECURITY QUESTIONNAIRE *(DD 98)*

ARMED FORCES SECURITY QUESTIONNAIRE

I - EXPLANATION

1. The interest of National Security require that all persons being considered for membership or retention in the Armed Forces be reliable, trustworthy, of good character, and of complete and unswerving loyalty to the United States. Accordingly, it is necessary for you to furnish information concerning your security qualifications. The answers which you give will be used in determining whether you are eligible for membership in the Armed Forces, in selection of your duty assignment, and for such other action as may be appropriate.

2. You are advised that in accordance with the Fifth Amendment of the Constitution of the United States you

cannot be compelled to furnish any statement which you may reasonably believe may lead to your prosecution for a crime. This is the only reason for which you may avail yourself of the privilege afforded by the Fifth Amendment in refusing to answer questions under Part IV below. Claiming the Fifth Amendment will not by itself constitute sufficient grounds to exempt you from military service for reasons of security. You are not required to answer any question in this questionnaire, the answer to which might be incriminating. If you do claim the privilege granted by the Fifth Amendment in refusing to answer any question, you should make a statement to that effect after the question involved.

II - ORGANIZATIONS OF SECURITY SIGNIFICANCE

1. There is set forth below a list of names of organizations, groups, and movements, reported by the Attorney General of the United States as having significance in connection with the national security. Please examine the list carefully, and note those organizations, and organizations of similar names, with which you are familiar. Then answer the questions set forth in Part IV below.

2. Your statement concerning membership or other association, with one or more of the organizations named may not, of itself, cause you to be ineligible for acceptance or retention in the Armed Forces.

Your age at the time of such association, circumstances prompting it, and the extent and frequency of involvement, are all highly pertinent, and will be fully weighed. Set forth all such factors under "Remarks" below, and continue on separate attached sheets of paper if necessary.

3. If there is any doubt in your mind as to whether your name has been linked with one of the organizations named, or as to whether a particular association is "worth mentioning", make a full explanation under "Remarks".

Organizations designated by the Attorney General, pursuant to Executive Order 10450, are listed below:

Communist Party, U. S. A., its subdivisions, subsidiaries and affiliates.

Communist Political Association, its subdivisions, subsidiaries and affiliates, including—

Alabama People's Educational Association

Florida Press and Educational League.

Oklahoma League for Political Education.

American Russian Institute, Philadelphia.

American Russian Institute of San Francisco.

American Russian Institute of Southern California, Los Angeles.

American Slav Congress.

American Youth for Peace.

American Youth Congress.

Civil Rights Congress for Texas.

Veterans Against Discrimination of Civil Rights Congress of New York.

Colombians.

Comte Coordinator Pro Republico Espanola.

Comte Pro Derechos Civiles.

Committee to Abolish Discrimination in Maryland.

Young Communist League.
Abraham Lincoln Brigade.
Abraham Lincoln School, Chicago, Illinois.
Action Committee to Free Spain Now.
American Association for Reconstruction in Yugoslavia, Inc.
American Branch of the Federation of Greek Maritime Unions.
American Christian Nationalist Party.
American Committee for European Workers' Relief.
American Committee for Protection of Foreign Born.
American Committee for the Settlement of Jews in Birobidjan, Inc.
American Committee for Spanish Freedom.
American Committee for Yugoslav Relief, Inc.
American Committee to Survey Labor Conditions in Europe.
American Council for a Democratic Greece, (formerly known as the Greek American Council; Greek American Committee for National Unity.
American Council on Soviet Relations.
American Croatian Congress.
American Jewish Labor Council.
American League Against War and Fascism.
American League for Peace and Democracy.
American National Labor Party.
American National Socialist League.
American National Socialist Party.
American Nationalist Party.
American Patriots, Inc.
American Peace Crusade.
American Peace Mobilization.
American Poles for Peace.
American Polish Labor Council.
American Polish League.
American Rescue Ship Mission (a project of the United American Spanish Aid Committee).
American-Russian Fraternal Society.
American-Russian Institute, New York (also known as the American Russian Institute for Cultural Relations with the Soviet Union).

Association of Georgia Klans.
Association of German Nationals (Reichsdeutsche Vereinigung).
Ausland-Organisation der NSDAP, Overseas Branch of Nazi Party.
Baltimore Forum.
Benjamin Davis Freedom Committee.
Black Dragon Society.
Boston School for Marxist Studies, Boston, Massachusetts.
Bridges-Robertson-Schmidt Defense Committee.
Bulgarian American People's League of the United States of America.
California Emergency Defense Committee.
California Labor School, Inc., 321 Divisadero Street, San Francisco, California.
Carpatho-Russian People's Society.
Central Council of American Women of Croatian Descent (also known as Central Council of American Croatian Women, National Council of Croatian Women).
Central Japanese Defense Association (British Chao Nippon Kai).
Central Japanese Association of Southern California.
Central Organization of the German-American National Alliance (Deutscher-Amerikanischer Einheitsfront).
Cervantes Fraternal Society.
China Welfare Appeal, Inc.
Chopin Cultural Center.
Citizens Committee to Free Earl Browder.
Citizens Committee for Harry Bridges.
Citizens Committee of the Upper West Side (New York City).
Citizens Emergency Defense Conference.
Citizens Protective League.
Civil Liberties Sponsoring Committee of Pittsburgh.
Civil Rights Congress and its affiliated organizations, including:

Committee for a Democratic Far Eastern Policy.
Committee for Constitutional and Political Freedom.
Committee for the Defense of the Pittsburgh Six.
Committee for Nationalist Action.
Committee for the Negro in the Arts.
Committee for Peace and Brotherhood Festival in Philadelphia.
Committee for the Protection of the Bill of Rights.
Committee for World Youth Friendship and Cultural Exchange.
Committee to Defend Marie Richardson.
Committee to Uphold the Bill of Rights.
Commonwealth College, Mena, Arkansas.
Congress Against Discrimination.
Congress of the Unemployed.
Connecticut Committee to Aid Victims of the Smith Act.
Connecticut State Youth Conference.
Congress of American Revolutionary Writers.
Congress of American Women.
Council on African Affairs.
Council of Greek Americans.
Council for Jobs, Relief, and Housing.
Council for Pan-American Democracy.
Croatian Benevolent Fraternity.
Dai Nippon Butoku Kai (Military Virtue Society of Japan or Military Art Society of Japan).
Daily Worker Press Club.
Daniels Defense Committee.
Dante Alighieri Society (Between 1935 and 1940).
Dennis Defense Committee.
Detroit Youth Assembly.
East Bay Peace Committee.
Eleanore Progressive League.
Emergency Conference to Save Spanish Refugees (founding body of the North American Spanish Aid Committee).
Everybody's Committee to Outlaw War.
Families of the Baltimore Smith Act Victims.
Families of the Smith Act Victims.

(Appendix 6 continued pp. 154–55.)

Federation of Italian War Veterans in the U.S.A., Inc. (*Associazione Nazionale Combattenti Italiani, Federazione degli Stati Uniti d' America*).

Finnish-American Mutual Aid Society.

Florida Press and Educational League.

Frederick Douglass Educational Center.

Freedom Stage, Inc.

Friends of the New Germany (*Freunde des Neuen Deutschland*).

Friends of the Soviet Union.

Garibaldi American Fraternal Society.

George Washington Carver School, New York City.

German-American Bund (*Amerika-deutscher Volksbund*).

German-American Republican League.

German-American Vocational League (*Deutsche-Amerikanische Berufsgemeinschaft*).

Guardian Club.

Harlem Trade Union Council.

Hawaii Civil Liberties Committee.

Heimusha Kai, also known as Nebuhei Heishi Gimushe Kai, Zaibei Nihonjin, Heijahn Gimusha Kai and Zaibei Heimusha Kai (*Japanese Residing in American Military Conscripts Association*).

Hinode Kai (*Imperial Japanese Reservists*).

Hinomaru Kai (*Rising Sun Flag Society - a group of Japanese War Veterans*).

Hokubei Zaigo Shoko Dan (*North American Reserve Officers Association*).

Hollywood Writers Mobilization for Defense.

Hungarian-American Council for Democracy.

Hungarian Brotherhood.

Idaho Pension Union.

Independent Party (*Seattle, Washington*).

Independent People's Party.

Industrial Workers of the World.

International Labor Defense.

International Workers Order, its subdivisions, subsidiaries and affiliation.

Japanese Association of America.

Japanese Overseas Central Society (*Kaigai Doho Chuo Kai*).

Japanese Overseas Convention, Tokyo, Japan, 1940.

Japanese Protective Association (*Recruiting

League of American Writers.

Lictor Society (*Italian Black Shirts*).

Macedonian-American People's League.

Mario Morgantini Circle.

Maritime Labor Committee to Defend Al Lannon.

Maryland Congress Against Discrimination.

Massachusetts Committee for the Bill of Rights.

Massachusetts Minute Women for Peace (*not connected with the Minute Women of the U.S.A., Inc.*).

Maurice Braverman Defense Committee.

Michigan Civil Rights Federation.

Michigan Council for Peace.

Michigan School of Social Science.

Nanka Teikoku Gunyudan (*Imperial Military Friends Group or Southern California War Veterans*).

National Association of Mexican Americans (*also National Association of Mexican Americans*).

National Blue Star Mothers of America (*not to be confused with the Blue Star Mothers of America organized in February 1942*).

National Committee for the Defense of Political Prisoners.

National Committee to Win the Peace.

National Conference on American Policy in China and the Far East. (*a Conference called by the Committee for a Democratic Far Eastern Policy*).

National Council of Americans of Croatian Descent.

National Council of American-Soviet Friendship.

National Federation for Constitutional Liberties.

National Labor Conference for Peace.

National Negro Congress.

National Negro Labor Council.

Nationalist Action League.

Nationalist Party of Puerto Rico.

Nature Friends of America (*Since 1935*).

Negro Labor Victory Committee.

New Committee for Publications.

Nichibei Kogyo Kaisha (*The Great Fujii Theatre*).

North American Committee to Aid Spanish Democracy.

North American Spanish Aid Committee.

North Philadelphia Forum.

Northwest Japanese Association.

Progressive German-Americans, also known as Proletarian German-Americans of Chicago.

Proletarian Party of America.

Protestant War Veterans of the United States, Inc.

Provisional Committee of Citizens for Peace, Southwest Area.

Provisional Committee on Latin American Affairs.

Provisional Committee to Abolish Discrimination in the State of Maryland.

Puerto Rican Comite Pro Libertades Civiles (CLC)

Puertorriqenos Unidos (Puerto Ricans United)

ugd City Committee for Peace.

Quenabridge Tenants League.

Revolutionary Workers League.

Romanian American Fraternal Society.

Russian American Society, Inc.

Sakura Kai (*Patriotic Society or Cherry Association of Japanese War Veterans or the Nan-Japanese War*).

Samuel Adams School, Boston, Mass.

Santa Barbara Peace Forum.

Schappes Defense Committee.

Schneiderman-Darcy Defense Committee.

School of Jewish Studies, New York City.

Seattle Labor School, Seattle, Washington.

Serbian Vidovdan Council.

Shinto Templo (*Limited to State Shinto abolished in 1945*).

Silver Shirt Legion of America.

Slavic Council of Southern California.

Slovak Workers Society.

Slovenian-American National Council.

Socialist Workers Party, including American Committee for European Workers' Relief.

Sokoku Kai (*Fatherland Society*).

Southern Negro Youth Congress.

Suiko Sha (*Reserve Officers Association, Los Angeles*).

Syracuse Women for Peace.

Tom Paine School of Social Science, Philadelphia, Pennsylvania.

Tom Paine School of Westchester, New York.

Trade Union Committee for Peace.

Trade Unionists for Peace.

Tri-State Negro Trade Union Council.

Ukrainian-American Fraternal Union.

Union of American Croatians.

Union of New York Veterans.

Jefferson School of Social Science, New York City.
Jewish Culture Society.
Jewish People's Committee.
Jewish People's Fraternal Order.
Jibyuto Lit Kai (The Committee for the Crisis).
Johnson-Forest Group.
Joint Anti-Fascist Refugee Committee.
Joint Council of Progressive Italian-American, Inc.
Joseph Weydemeyer School of Social Science, St. Louis, Missouri.
Kibei Seinen Kai (Association of U.S. citizens of Japanese ancestry who have returned to America after studying in Japan).
Knights of the White Camelia.
Ku Klux Klan.
Kyffhaeuser, also known as Kyffhaeuser League (Kryffhaeuser Bund) Kyffhaeuser Fellowship (Kryffhaeuser Kameradschaft); Kyffhaeuser War Relief (Kryffhaeuser Kriegshilfswerk)
Labor Council for Negro Rights.
Labor Research Association, Inc.
Labor Youth League.
League for Common Sense.

Oklahoma Committee to Defend Political Prisoners.
Oklahoma League for Political Education.
Original Southern Klans, Incorporated.
Pacific Northwest Labor School, Seattle, Washington.
Palo Alto Peace Club.
Partido del Pueblo of Panam (operating in the Canal Zone).
Peace Information Center.
Peace Movement of Ethiopia.
People's Drama, Inc.
People's Educational and Press Association of Texas.
People's Educational Association (Incorporated under ... as Los Angeles Educational Association, Inc.; also known as People's Educational Center.
People's Institute of Applied Religion.
People's Program (Seattle, Washington), also known as People's School.
People's Radio Foundation, Inc.
People's Rights Party.
Philadelphia Labor Committee for Negro Rights.
Philadelphia School of Social Science and Art.
Pittsburgh Arts Club (New York City)
Poca League (New York City)
Political Prisoners' Welfare Committee.
Polonia Society of the IWO.

United Committee of Jewish Societies and Landsmanschaft Federation, also known as Coordination Committee of Jewish Landsmanschaften and Fraternal Organizations.
United ... of ... Slavic Americans.
United Defense Council of Southern California.
United Harlem Tenants and Consumers Organization.
United May Day Committee.
United Negro and Allied Veterans of America.
Veterans Against Discrimination of Civil Rights Congress of New York.
Veterans of the Abraham Lincoln Brigade.
Virginia League for People's Education.
Voice of Freedom Committee.
Walt Whitman School of Social Science, Newark, New Jersey.
Washington Bookshop Association.
Washington Committee to Defend the Bill of Rights.
Washington Committee for Democratic Action.
Washington Commonwealth Federation.
Washington Pension Union.
Wisconsin Conference on Social Legislation.
Workers Alliance (since April 1936).
Yiddisher Kultur Farband.
Yugoslav-American Cooperative Home, Inc.
Yugoslav Seamen's Club, Inc.

III - INSTRUCTIONS

1. Set forth an explanation for each answer checked "Yes" under question 2 below under "Remarks". Attach as many extra sheets as necessary for a full explanation, signing or initialing each extra sheet.

2. Title 18, U.S. Code, Section 1001, provides, in pertinent part: "Whoever ... (falsifies, conceals or covers up ... or makes any false ... statements ... or makes or uses any false writing ... shall be fined not more than $10,000 or imprisoned not more than five years, or both". Any false, fraudulent or fictitious response to the questions under Title Part IV below may give rise to criminal liability under Title 18, U.S.C. Section 1001. You are advised, however, that you

will not incur each liability unless you supply inaccurate statements with knowledge of their untruthfulness. You are therefore advised that before you sign this form and turn it in to Selective Service or military authorities, you should be sure that it is truthful; that detailed explanations are given for each "Yes" answer under question 2 of Part IV below, and that details given are as full and complete as you can make them.

3. In stating details, it is permissible, if your memory is hazy on particular points, to use such expressions as "I think", "in my opinion", "I believe", or "to the best of my recollection".

(Appendix 6 continued pp.156–57.)

(*Appendix 6 continued.*)

IV – QUESTIONS

(For each answer checked "Yes" under question 2 set forth a full explanation under "Remarks" below)

Question	YES	NO
1. I have read the list of names of organizations, groups, and movements set forth under Part II of this form and the explanation which precedes it.		
2. Concerning the list of organizations, groups and movements set forth under Part II above:		
a. Are you now a member of any of the organizations, groups, or movements listed?		▓
b. Have you ever been a member of any of the organizations, groups, or movements listed?		
c. Are you now employed by any of the organizations, groups, or movements listed?		
d. Have you ever been employed by any of the organizations, groups, or movements listed?		
e. Have you ever attended any meeting of any of the organizations, groups, or movements listed?		
j. Have you ever contributed money to any of the organizations, groups, or movements listed?		
k. Have you ever contributed services to any of the organizations, groups, or movements listed?		
l. Have you ever subscribed to any publication of any of the organizations, groups, or movements listed?		
m. Have you ever been employed by a foreign government or any agency thereof?		
n. Are you now a member of the Communist Party of any foreign country?		
o. Have you ever been a member of the Communist Party of any foreign country?		
p. Have you ever been the subject of a loyalty or security hearing?		

156

q. Are you now or have you ever been a member of any organization, association, movement, group or combination of persons not on the Attorney General's list which advocates the overthrow of our constitutional form of government, or which has adopted the policy of advocating or approving the commission of acts of force or violence to deny other persons their rights under the Constitution of the United States, or which seeks to alter the form of government of the United States by unconstitutional means?

r. Have you ever been known by any other last name than that used in signing this questionnaire?

f. Have you ever attended any social gathering of any of the organizations, groups, or movements listed?

g. Have you ever attended any gathering of any kind sponsored by any of the organizations, groups, or movements listed?

h. Have you ever prepared material for publication by any of the organizations, groups, or movements listed?

i. Have you ever corresponded with any of the organizations, groups, or movements listed or with any publication thereof?

REMARKS

(Appendix 6 continued pp. 158–59.)

(Appendix 6 continued.)

REMARKS (Continued)

158

CERTIFICATION

IN REGARD TO ANY PART OF THIS QUESTIONNAIRE CONCERNING WHICH I HAVE HAD ANY QUESTION AS TO THE MEANING, I HAVE REQUESTED AND HAVE OBTAINED A COMPLETE EXPLANATION. I CERTIFY THAT THE STATEMENTS MADE BY ME UNDER PART IV ABOVE AND ON ANY SUPPLEMENTAL PAGES HERETO ATTACHED, ARE FULL, TRUE, AND CORRECT.

TYPED FULL NAME OF PERSON MAKING CERTIFICATION	SERVICE NUMBER (If any)	SIGNATURE OF PERSON MAKING CERTIFICATION
TYPED NAME OF WITNESS	DATE	SIGNATURE OF WITNESS

159

STATEMENT OF PERSONAL HISTORY (DD 398)

STATEMENT OF PERSONAL HISTORY

INSTRUCTIONS: Read the certification at the end of this questionnaire before entering the required data. Print or type all answers. All questions and statements must be completed. If the answer is "None," so state. Do not misstate or omit material fact since the statements made herein are subject to verification. If more space is needed, use the Remarks section, item 20, and attach additional sheets if necessary. The information entered herein is for official use only and will be maintained in confidence.

1. *(Print)* FIRST NAME—MIDDLE NAME—MAIDEN NAME *(If any)*—LAST NAME

☐ MR.
☐ MRS.
☐ MISS

2. STATUS

CIVILIAN	MILITARY ON ACTIVE DUTY

3. ALIAS(ES), NICKNAME(S), OR CHANGES IN NAME *(Other than by marriage)*

4. PERMANENT MAILING ADDRESS

5. DATE OF BIRTH *(Day, month, year)* | PLACE OF BIRTH *(City, County, State, and Country)* | PLACE CERTIFICATE RECORDED

HEIGHT	WEIGHT	COLOR OF EYES	COLOR OF HAIR	SCARS, PHYSICAL DEFECTS, DISTINGUISHING MARKS

6. DO YOU HAVE A HISTORY OF MENTAL OR NERVOUS DISORDERS? ☐ YES ☐ NO   ARE YOU NOW OR HAVE YOU EVER BEEN ADDICTED TO THE USE OF HABIT FORMING DRUGS SUCH AS NARCOTICS OR BARBITURATES? ☐ YES ☐ NO   ARE YOU NOW OR HAVE YOU EVER BEEN A CHRONIC USER TO EXCESS OF ALCOHOLIC BEVERAGES? ☐ YES ☐ NO   IF THE ANSWER TO ANY OF THE ABOVE IS "YES." EXPLAIN IN ITEM 20

7. U.S. CITIZEN ☐

	NATIVE	IF NATURALIZED, CERTIFICATE NO.	IF DERIVED, PARENTS' CERTIFICATE NO(S)	DATE, PLACE, AND COURT
NATIVE	☐			
YES	☐			
NO	☐			

ALIEN ☐ | REGISTRATION NO | NATIVE COUNTRY | DATE AND PORT OF ENTRY | DO YOU INTEND TO BECOME A U.S. CITIZEN? ☐ YES ☐ NO

8.

MILITARY SERVICE

ARE YOU PRESENTLY ON ACTIVE DUTY IN THE U.S. ARMED FORCES DRAWING FULL PAY? ☐ YES ☐ NO   IF "YES," COMPLETE THE FOLLOWING:

GRADE AND SERVICE NO.	SERVICE AND COMPONENT	ORGANIZATION AND STATION	DATE CURRENT ACTIVE SERVICE STARTED

ARE YOU PRESENTLY A MEMBER OF A U.S. RESERVE OR NATIONAL GUARD ORGANIZATION? ☐ YES ☐ NO   IF "YES," COMPLETE THE FOLLOWING:

GRADE AND SERVICE NO.	SERVICE AND COMPONENT	ORGANIZATION AND STATION ON UNIT AND LOCATION

9. EDUCATION (Account for all civilian schools and military academies. Do not include service schools)

MONTH AND YEAR		NAME AND LOCATION OF SCHOOL	GRADUATE		DEGREE
FROM—	TO—		YES	NO	

10. FAMILY (List in order given, parents, spouse, guardians, foster parents, stepparents, parents-in-law, former spouse(s) (if divorced give date and place), children, brothers and sisters, even though deceased. Include any others you resided with or with whom a close relationship existed or exists. If the person is not a U.S. citizen by birth, give date and port of entry, alien registration number, naturalization certificate number and place of issuance.)

RELATION AND NAME	DATE AND PLACE OF BIRTH	PRESENT ADDRESS, IF LIVING	U. S. CITIZEN	
			YES	NO
FATHER				
MOTHER (Maiden name)				
SPOUSE (Maiden name)				
OTHER (Specify)				

DD FORM 398
1 MAR 64

REPLACES EDITION OF 1 MAY 55, WHICH MAY BE USED.

Exception to Standard Form 86
Approved by Bureau of the Budget July 1963

(Appendix 7 continued pp. 162–63.)

11. OTHER RELATIVES AND ALIEN FRIENDS LIVING IN FOREIGN COUNTRIES (*List grandparents, first cousins, aunts, uncles, brothers- and sisters-in-law, and other persons with whom a close relationship existed or exists*)

RELATIONSHIP AND NAME	AGE	OCCUPATION	ADDRESS	CITIZENSHIP

12. FOREIGN TRAVEL (*Other than as a direct result of United States military duties*)

DATES		COUNTRY VISITED	PURPOSE OF TRAVEL
FROM—	TO—		

13. EMPLOYMENT (*Show every employment you have had and all periods of unemployment*)

MONTH AND YEAR		NAME AND ADDRESS OF EMPLOYER	NAME OF IMMEDIATE SUPERVISOR	REASON FOR LEAVING
FROM—	TO—			

SOCIAL SECURITY NO.

DID ANY OF THE ABOVE EMPLOYMENTS REQUIRE A SECURITY CLEARANCE? ☐ YES ☐ NO   DO YOU HAVE ANY FOREIGN PROPERTY OR BUSINESS CONNECTIONS, OR HAVE YOU EVER BEEN EMPLOYED BY A FOREIGN GOVERNMENT, FIRM, OR AGENCY? ☐ YES ☐ NO   HAVE YOU EVER BEEN REFUSED BOND? ☐ YES ☐ NO   IF THE ANSWER TO ANY OF THE ABOVE IS "YES," EXPLAIN IN ITEM 20

14. CREDIT AND CHARACTER REFERENCES (Do not include relatives, former employers, or persons living outside the United States or its Territories.)

	NAME (List 3 credit and 3 character)	YEARS KNOWN	STREET AND NUMBER (Business address preferred)	CITY	STATE OR TERRITORY
CREDIT					
CHARACTER					

(Appendix 7 continued pp. 164–65.)

163

(Appendix 7 continued.)

15. LIST ALL RESIDENCES FROM 1 JANUARY 1937

MONTH AND YEAR		STREET AND NUMBER	CITY	STATE OR COUNTRY
FROM—	TO—			

16. PAST AND/OR PRESENT MEMBERSHIP IN ORGANIZATIONS

NAME AND ADDRESS	TYPE (Social, fraternal, professional, etc.)	OFFICE HELD	MEMBERSHIP	
			FROM—	TO—

17.

	ARE YOU NOW OR HAVE YOU EVER BEEN A MEMBER OF THE COMMUNIST PARTY U. S. A., OR ANY COMMUNIST ORGANIZATIONS ANYWHERE?
	ARE YOU NOW OR HAVE YOU EVER BEEN A MEMBER OF A FASCIST ORGANIZATION?
	ARE YOU NOW OR HAVE YOU EVER BEEN A MEMBER OF ANY ORGANIZATION, ASSOCIATION, MOVEMENT, GROUP OR COMBINATION OF PERSONS WHICH ADVOCATED THE OVERTHROW OF OUR CONSTITUTIONAL FORM OF GOVERNMENT, OR WHICH HAS ADOPTED THE POLICY OF ADVOCATING OR APPROVING THE COMMISSION OF ACTS OF FORCE OR VIOLENCE TO DENY OTHER PERSONS THEIR RIGHTS UNDER THE CONSTITUTION OF THE UNITED STATES, OR WHICH SEEKS TO ALTER THE FORM OF GOVERNMENT OF THE UNITED STATES BY UNCONSTITUTIONAL MEANS?
	ARE YOU NOW OR HAVE YOU EVER BEEN AFFILIATED OR ASSOCIATED WITH ANY ORGANIZATION OF THE TYPE DESCRIBED ABOVE AS AN AGENT, OFFICIAL, OR EMPLOYEE?
	ARE YOU NOW ASSOCIATING WITH, OR HAVE YOU ASSOCIATED WITH ANY INDIVIDUALS, INCLUDING RELATIVES, WHO YOU KNOW OR HAVE REASON TO BELIEVE, ARE OR HAVE BEEN MEMBERS OF ANY OF THE ORGANIZATIONS IDENTIFIED ABOVE?
	HAVE YOU EVER ENGAGED IN ANY OF THE FOLLOWING ACTIVITIES OF ANY ORGANIZATION OF THE TYPE DESCRIBED ABOVE: CONTRIBUTION(S) TO, ATTENDANCE AT OR PARTICIPATION IN ANY ORGANIZATIONAL, SOCIAL, OR OTHER ACTIVITIES OF SAID ORGANIZATIONS OR OF ANY PROJECTS SPONSORED BY THEM: THE SALE, GIFT, OR DISTRIBUTION OF ANY WRITTEN, PRINTED, OR OTHER MATTER, PREPARED, REPRODUCED, OR PUBLISHED, BY THEM OR ANY OF THEIR AGENTS OR INSTRUMENTALITIES?
	IF "YES," DESCRIBE THE CIRCUMSTANCES. ATTACH ADDITIONAL SHEETS FOR A FULL DETAILED STATEMENT. IF ASSOCIATED WITH ANY OF THE ABOVE ORGANIZATIONS, SPECIFY NATURE AND EXTENT OF ASSOCIATION WITH EACH, INCLUDING OFFICE OR POSITION HELD. ALSO INCLUDE DATES, PLACES, AND CREDENTIALS NOW OR FORMERLY HELD. IF ASSOCIATIONS HAVE BEEN WITH INDIVIDUALS WHO ARE MEMBERS OF THE ABOVE ORGANIZATIONS, THEN LIST THE INDIVIDUALS AND THE ORGANIZATIONS WITH WHICH THEY WERE OR ARE AFFILIATED.
18	HAVE YOU EVER BEEN DETAINED, HELD, ARRESTED, INDICTED OR SUMMONED INTO COURT AS A DEFENDANT IN A CRIMINAL PROCEEDING, OR CONVICTED, FINED, OR IMPRISONED OR PLACED ON PROBATION, OR HAVE YOU EVER BEEN ORDERED TO DEPOSIT BAIL OR COLLATERAL FOR THE VIOLATION OF ANY LAW, POLICE REGULATION OR ORDINANCE (*excluding minor traffic violations for which a fine or forfeiture of $25, or less was imposed*)? INCLUDE ALL COURT MARTIALS WHILE IN MILITARY SERVICE. ☐ YES ☐ NO IF "YES," LIST THE DATE, THE NATURE OF THE OFFENSE OR VIOLATION, THE NAME AND LOCATION OF THE COURT OR PLACE OF HEARING, AND THE PENALTY IMPOSED OR OTHER DISPOSITION OF EACH CASE.

(Appendix 7 continued pp. 166–67.)

(Appendix 7 continued.)

19. ARE THERE ANY INCIDENTS IN YOUR LIFE NOT MENTIONED HEREIN WHICH MAY REFLECT UPON YOUR LOYALTY TO THE UNITED STATES OR UPON YOUR SUITABILITY TO PERFORM THE DUTIES WHICH YOU MAY BE CALLED UPON TO TAKE OR WHICH MIGHT REQUIRE FURTHER EXPLANATION? ☐ YES ☐ NO   IF "YES" GIVE DETAILS

20. REMARKS

I CERTIFY THAT THE ENTRIES MADE BY ME ABOVE ARE TRUE, COMPLETE, AND CORRECT TO THE BEST OF MY KNOWLEDGE AND BELIEF AND ARE MADE IN GOOD FAITH. I UNDERSTAND THAT A KNOWING AND WILLFUL FALSE STATEMENT ON THIS FORM CAN BE PUNISHED BY FINE OR IMPRISONMENT OR BOTH (See U. S. Code, title 18, section 1001)

DATE	SIGNATURE OF PERSON COMPLETING FORM	
	TYPED NAME AND ADDRESS OF WITNESS	SIGNATURE OF WITNESS

2. *THIS SECTION TO BE COMPLETED BY AUTHORITY REQUESTING INVESTIGATION*

BRIEF DESCRIPTION OF DUTY ASSIGNMENT AND DEGREE OF CLASSIFIED MATTER (top secret, secret, etc.) TO WHICH APPLICANT WILL REQUIRE ACCESS

RECORD OF PRIOR CLEARANCES

DATE OF CLEARANCE	TYPE OF CLEARANCE	AGENCY THAT COMPLETED INVESTIGATION

REMARKS

Appendix 8
JOINT MOTION MEASUREMENT

JOINT MOTION MEASUREMENT
(TM 8-640)

1. THE HIP

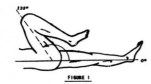

FIGURE 1

2. THE KNEE

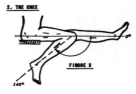

FIGURE 3

FLEXION

a - *POSITION* - Supine, knee flexed; opposite knee and hip straight
b - *STATIONARY ARM* - Parallel to long axis of trunk.
c - *MOVING ARM* - In line with lateral midline of femur.

EXTENSION AND FLEXION

a - *POSITION* - Sitting with knee flexed.
b - *STATIONARY ARM* - Parallel to femur on a line from the lateral condyle to greater trochanter.
c - *MOVING ARM* - Parallel to fibula on line with lateral malleolus.

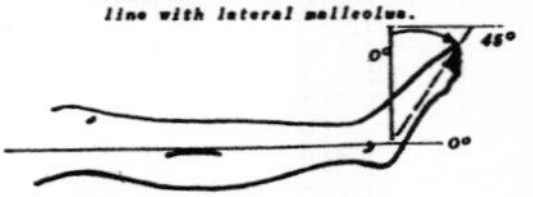

FIGURE 2

FIGURE 4

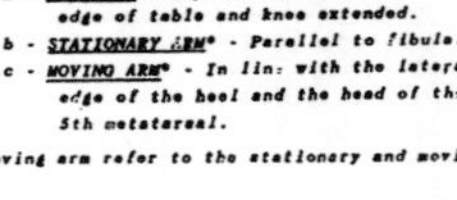

FIGURE 5

EXTENSION

a - *POSITION* - Prone
b - *STATIONARY ARM* - Parallel to long axis of trunk.
c - *MOVING ARM* - In line with lateral midline of femur.

PLANTAR FLEXION & DORSIFLEXION

a - *POSITION* - Supine with heel over edge of table and knee extended.
b - *STATIONARY ARM* - Parallel to fibula.
c - *MOVING ARM* - In line with the lateral edge of the heel and the head of the 5th metatarsal.

(*) *For purposes of this regulation, stationary arm and moving arm refer to the stationary and moving portions of the goniometer.*

JOINT MOTION MEASUREMENT – Cont.

4. THE SHOULDER

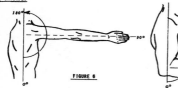

FIGURE 6

FLEXION

   a - *POSITION* - Standing, sitting or supine with elbow extended. Palm facing medially. Measure .. on lateral aspect of body.

   b - *STATIONARY ARM* - Along mid-axillary line of trunk.

   c - *MOVING ARM* - Along lateral midline of humerus.

5. THE ELBOW

FIGURE 8

EXTENSION AND FLEXION

   a - *POSITION* - Standing, sitting or supine. Forearm in mid-position between supination and pronation

   b - *STATIONARY ARM* - Along midline of humerus:

   c - *MOVING ARM* - Along midline of forsal aspect of forearm.

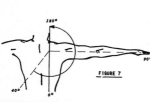

FIGURE 7

ADDUCTION AND ABDUCTION

   a - *POSITION* - Standing or sitting.

   b - *STATIONARY ARM* - Parallel to spine but at lateral aspect of body.

   c - *MOVING ARM* - Parallel to midline of humerus toward olecranon process.

6. THE WRIST

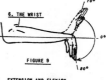

FIGURE 9

EXTENSION AND FLEXION

   a - *POSITION* - Sitting or standing with elbow flexed and forearm in pronation.

   b - *STATIONARY ARM* - Along lateral midline of forearm.

   c - *MOVING ARM* - Parallel to 5th metacarpal.

(*) For purposes of this regulation, stationary arm and moving arm refer to the stationary and moving portions of the goniometer.

A4-2

Appendix 9

RANDOM SELECTION SEQUENCE 1970

January	February	March	April	May	June
1 - 305	1 - 86	1 - 108	1 - 32	1 - 330	1 - 249
2 - 159	2 - 144	2 - 29	2 - 271	2 - 298	2 - 228
3 - 251	3 - 297	3 - 267	3 - 83	3 - 40	3 - 301
4 - 215	4 - 210	4 - 275	4 - 81	4 - 276	4 - 20
5 - 101	5 - 214	5 - 293	5 - 269	5 - 364	5 - 28
6 - 224	6 - 347	6 - 139	6 - 253	6 - 155	6 - 110
7 - 306	7 - 91	7 - 122	7 - 147	7 - 35	7 - 85
8 - 199	8 - 181	8 - 213	8 - 312	8 - 321	8 - 366
9 - 194	9 - 338	9 - 317	9 - 219	9 - 197	9 - 335
10 - 325	10 - 216	10 - 323	10 - 218	10 - 65	10 - 206
11 - 329	11 - 150	11 - 136	11 - 14	11 - 37	11 - 134
12 - 221	12 - 68	12 - 300	12 - 346	12 - 133	12 - 272
13 - 318	13 - 152	13 - 259	13 - 124	13 - 295	13 - 69
14 - 238	14 - 4	14 - 354	14 - 231	14 - 178	14 - 356
15 - 17	15 - 89	15 - 169	15 - 273	15 - 130	15 - 180
16 - 121	16 - 212	16 - 166	16 - 148	16 - 55	16 - 274
17 - 235	17 - 189	17 - 33	17 - 260	17 - 112	17 - 73
18 - 140	18 - 292	18 - 332	18 - 90	18 - 278	18 - 341
19 - 58	19 - 25	19 - 200	19 - 336	19 - 75	19 - 104
20 - 280	20 - 302	20 - 239	20 - 345	20 - 183	20 - 360
21 - 186	21 - 363	21 - 334	21 - 62	21 - 250	21 - 60
22 - 337	22 - 290	22 - 265	22 - 316	22 - 326	22 - 247
23 - 118	23 - 57	23 - 256	23 - 252	23 - 319	23 - 109
24 - 59	24 - 236	24 - 258	24 - 2	24 - 31	24 - 358
25 - 52	25 - 179	25 - 343	25 - 351	25 - 361	25 - 137
26 - 92	26 - 365	26 - 170	26 - 340	26 - 357	26 - 22
27 - 355	27 - 205	27 - 268	27 - 74	27 - 296	27 - 64
28 - 77	28 - 299	28 - 223	28 - 262	28 - 308	28 - 222
29 - 349	29 - 285	29 - 362	29 - 191	29 - 226	29 - 353
30 - 164		30 - 217	30 - 208	30 - 103	30 - 209
31 - 211		31 - 30		31 - 313	

July	August	September	October	November	December
1 - 93	1 - 111	1 - 225	1 - 359	1 - 19	1 - 129
2 - 350	2 - 45	2 - 161	2 - 125	2 - 34	2 - 328
3 - 115	3 - 261	3 - 49	3 - 244	3 - 348	3 - 157
4 - 279	4 - 145	4 - 232	4 - 202	4 - 266	4 - 165
5 - 188	5 - 54	5 - 82	5 - 24	5 - 310	5 - 56
6 - 327	6 - 114	6 - 6	6 - 87	6 - 76	6 - 10
7 - 50	7 - 168	7 - 8	7 - 234	7 - 51	7 - 12
8 - 13	8 - 48	8 - 184	8 - 283	8 - 97	8 - 105
9 - 277	9 - 106	9 - 263	9 - 342	9 - 80	9 - 43
10 - 284	10 - 21	10- 71	10 - 220	10 - 282	10 - 41
11 - 248	11 - 324	11 - 158	11 - 237	11 - 46	11 - 39
12 - 15	12 - 142	12 - 242	12 - 72	12 - 66	12 - 314
13 - 42	13 - 307	13 - 175	13 - 138	13 - 126	13 - 163
14 - 331	14 - 198	14 - 1	14 - 294	14 - 127	14 - 26
15 - 322	15 - 102	15 - 113	15 - 171	15 - 131	15 - 320
16 - 120	16 - 44	16 - 207	16 - 254	16 - 107	16 - 96
17 - 98	17 - 154	17 - 255	17 - 288	17 - 143	17 - 304
18 - 190	18 - 141	18 - 246	18 - 5	18 - 146	18 - 128
19 - 227	19 - 311	19 - 177	19 - 241	19 - 203	19 - 240
20 - 187	20 - 344	20 - 63	20 - 192	20 - 185	20 - 135
21 - 27	21 - 291	21 - 204	21 - 243	21 - 156	21 - 70
22 - 153	22 - 339	22 - 160	22 - 117	22 - 9	22 - 53
23 - 172	23 - 116	23 - 119	23 - 201	23 - 182	23 - 162
24 - 23	24 - 36	24 - 195	24 - 196	24 - 230	24 - 95
25 - 67	25 - 286	25 - 149	25 - 176	25 - 132	25 - 84
26 - 303	26 - 245	26 - 18	26 - 7	26 - 309	26 - 173
27 - 289	27 - 352	27 - 233	27 - 264	27 - 47	27 - 78
28 - 88	28 - 167	28 - 257	28 - 94	28 - 281	28 - 123
29 - 270	29 - 61	29 - 151	29 - 229	29 - 99	29 - 16
30 - 287	30 - 333	30 - 315	30 - 38	30 - 174	30 - 3
31 - 193	31 - 11		31 - 79		31 - 100

Under the new lottery system, youths will be drafted in the order their birthdays are picked in special annual drawings. Above is a complete list of the lottery numbers assigned in December 1969, to all those born between January 1, 1944, and December 31, 1950. For instance, a man born May 1 has number 330, and all eligible men with numbers 1-329 must be called before him.

January	February	March	April	May	June
1 - 133	1 - 335	1 - 14	1 - 224	1 - 179	1 - 65
2 - 195	2 - 354	2 - 77	2 - 216	2 - 96	2 - 304
3 - 336	3 - 186	3 - 207	3 - 297	3 - 171	3 - 135
4 - 99	4 - 94	4 - 117	4 - 37	4 - 240	4 - 42
5 - 33	5 - 97	5 - 299	5 - 124	5 - 301	5 - 233
6 - 285	6 - 16	6 - 296	6 - 312	6 - 268	6 - 153
7 - 159	7 - 25	7 - 141	7 - 142	7 - 29	7 - 169
8 - 116	8 - 127	8 - 79	8 - 267	8 - 105	8 - 7
9 - 53	9 - 187	9 - 278	9 - 223	9 - 357	9 - 352
10 - 101	10 - 46	10 - 150	10 - 165	10 - 146	10 - 76
11 - 144	11 - 227	11 - 317	11 - 178	11 - 293	11 - 355
12 - 152	12 - 262	12 - 24	12 - 89	12 - 210	12 - 51
13 - 330	13 - 13	13 - 241	13 - 143	13 - 353	13 - 342
14 - 71	14 - 260	14 - 12	14 - 202	14 - 40	14 - 363
15 - 75	15 - 201	15 - 157	15 - 182	15 - 344	15 - 276
16 - 136	16 - 334	16 - 258	16 - 31	16 - 175	16 - 229
17 - 54	17 - 345	17 - 220	17 - 264	17 - 212	17 - 289
18 - 185	18 - 337	18 - 319	18 - 138	18 - 180	18 - 214
19 - 188	19 - 331	19 - 189	19 - 62	19 - 155	19 - 163
20 - 211	20 - 20	20 - 170	20 - 118	20 - 242	20 - 43
21 - 129	21 - 213	21 - 246	21 - 8	21 - 225	21 - 113
22 - 132	22 - 271	22 - 269	22 - 256	22 - 199	22 - 307
23 - 48	23 - 351	23 - 281	23 - 292	23 - 222	23 - 44
24 - 177	24 - 226	24 - 203	24 - 244	24 - 22	24 - 236
25 - 57	25 - 325	25 - 298	25 - 328	25 - 26	25 - 327
26 - 140	26 - 86	26 - 121	26 - 137	26 - 148	26 - 308
27 - 173	27 - 66	27 - 254	27 - 235	27 - 122	27 - 55
28 - 346	28 - 234	28 - 95	28 - 82	28 - 9	28 - 215
29 - 277		29 - 147	29 - 111	29 - 61	29 - 154
30 - 112		30 - 56	30 - 358	30 - 209	30 - 217
31 - 60		31 - 38		31 - 350	

July	August	September	October	November	December
1 - 104	1 - 326	1 - 283	1 - 306	1 - 243	1 - 347
2 - 322	2 - 102	2 - 161	2 - 191	2 - 205	2 - 321
3 - 30	3 - 279	3 - 183	3 - 134	3 - 294	3 - 110
4 - 59	4 - 300	4 - 231	4 - 266	4 - 39	4 - 305
5 - 287	5 - 64	5 - 295	5 - 166	5 - 286	5 - 27
6 - 164	6 - 251	6 - 21	6 - 78	6 - 245	6 - 198
7 - 365	7 - 263	7 - 265	7 - 131	7 - 72	7 - 162
8 - 106	8 - 49	8 - 108	8 - 45	8 - 119	8 - 323
9 - 1	9 - 125	9 - 313	9 - 302	9 - 176	9 - 114
10 - 158	10 - 359	10 - 130	10 - 160	10 - 63	10 - 204
11 - 174	11 - 230	11 - 288	11 - 84	11 - 123	11 - 73
12 - 257	12 - 320	12 - 314	12 - 70	12 - 255	12 - 19
13 - 349	13 - 58	13 - 238	13 - 92	13 - 272	13 - 151
14 - 156	14 - 103	14 - 247	14 - 115	14 - 11	14 - 348
15 - 273	15 - 270	15 - 291	15 - 310	15 - 362	15 - 87
16 - 284	16 - 329	16 - 139	16 - 34	16 - 197	16 - 41
17 - 341	17 - 343	17 - 200	17 - 290	17 - 6	17 - 315
18 - 90	18 - 109	18 - 333	18 - 340	18 - 280	18 - 208
19 - 316	19 - 83	19 - 228	19 - 74	19 - 252	19 - 249
20 - 120	20 - 69	20 - 261	20 - 196	20 - 98	20 - 218
21 - 356	21 - 50	21 - 68	21 - 5	21 - 35	21 - 181
22 - 282	22 - 250	22 - 88	22 - 36	22 - 253	22 - 194
23 - 172	23 - 10	23 - 206	23 - 339	23 - 193	23 - 219
24 - 360	24 - 274	24 - 237	24 - 149	24 - 81	24 - 2
25 - 3	25 - 364	25 - 107	25 - 17	25 - 23	25 - 361
26 - 47	26 - 91	26 - 93	26 - 184	26 - 52	26 - 80
27 - 85	27 - 232	27 - 338	27 - 318	27 - 168	27 - 239
28 - 190	28 - 248	28 - 309	28 - 28	28 - 324	28 - 128
29 - 4	29 - 32	29 - 303	29 - 259	29 - 100	29 - 145
30 - 15	30 - 167	30 - 18	30 - 332	30 - 67	30 - 192
31 - 221	31 - 275		31 - 311		31 - 126

Above is a complete list of lottery numbers assigned July, 1970, to all young men born in 1951. Those affected by this lottery will be vulnerable to the draft during 1971.

MEDICAL COMMITTEE FOR HUMAN RIGHTS

The Medical Committee for Human Rights is an organization of radical doctors and other health workers sympathetic to the problems of draft-threatened youths. It is MCHR policy to provide free medical or psychiatric examinations for draft registrants who cannot afford the services of a private physician. The group's national headquarters has a temporary address at 1520 Naudain St., Philadelphia, Pa. 19146.

ATLANTA
130 Alden Ave. #801 (zip: 30309)
Contact: Dr. Bourne 404-872-1930

BALTIMORE
4424 Underwood Rd. (21218)
Contact: Dr. Furstenberg 301-366-0750 (office) or
889-5151 (home)

BOSTON
529 Massachusetts Ave. (02118)
Contact: 617-734-MCHR

CHICAGO
1512 East 55th St. (60615)
Contact: Dr. Young 312-HY-3-8212

CLEVELAND
2224 Elandon Dr. (Cleveland Hts., 44106)
Contact: Dr. Liebman 216-229-3612

DENVER
2508 East 11th St. (80206)

DETROIT
Gratiot P.O. Box 7758 (48207)
Contact: Miss Walls 313-964-2015 (home) or
874-0555 (office)

HARTFORD, Conn.
1823 Asylum Ave. (06117)
Contact: Dr. Schwartz 203-527-4880

LEXINGTON, Ky.
643 Gay Place No. (40505)
Contact: Miss Springham 606-333-0946

LITTLE ROCK, Ark.
Box 54 Univ. of Arkansas Medical Center (72201)
Contact: Mr. Payne 501-MO-4-5000 (ext. 856)

LOS ANGELES
P.O. Box 35204 or 6066 Cashil (90035)
Contact: 213-870-8006

MADISON, Wisc.
713 Olin Ave. (53715)

MIAMI
P.O. Box 1164 (Coral Gables, 33134)
Contact: Peace Center 305-443-9836

MINNEAPOLIS
2323 Clinton Ave. So., #204 (55404)
Contact: 612-338-8101

NASHVILLE
Box 199, Meharry Medical College (37202)
Contact: Mrs. Falk 615-297-0100

NEW HAVEN
333 Cedar Street (06510)
Contact: Rev. Duncombe 203-436-8354

NEW YORK CITY
135 West 4th St. (10012)
Contact: 212-254-4488 (M-W-F, 3-5 p.m.)

OAKLAND-BERKELEY
442 Beloit (Berkeley, 94708)
Contact: Dr. Nickels 415-526-1314

PHILADELPHIA
800 Addison St. (19147)
Contact: call phone information for new listing

PITTSBURGH
617 Empire Building (15222)
Contact: Mrs. Roth 412-681-1444 (home) or
391-1860 (office)

SAN DIEGO
P.O. Box 99011 (92109)
Contact: Dr. Abbott 714-488-4421 or
Mr. Reed 488-8001

SAN FRANCISCO
2519 Pacific Ave. (94115)
Contact: Dr. Frank 415-332-4798 (evenings) or
Medical Referral Service 415-362-0165

SEATTLE
4727 46th Ave. N.E. (98105)
Contact: Dr. Holcenberg 206-543-3268

SYRACUSE, N.Y.
503 So. Crouse (13210)
Contact: 315-476-DRUG

TUCSON, Ariz.
c/o B. Bruwer, Univ. of Arizona School of Medicine
(85721)
Contact: Dr. Bruwer 602-326-8872

WASHINGTON, D.C.
3410 Taylor Street (Chevy Chase, Md. 20015)
Contact: 301-654-3808